To Dorothy with
best wishes from
the author...

Wm H Bloom
June 6, 2001

Thanx for your interest in my
father's book. Please enjoy it.

Jonathan Bloom

Best wishes from the
author himself!
Wm H Bloom

After All, It's Only Brain Surgery

William Herman Bloom, M.D., F.A.C.S.

Noble House

Baltimore, Maryland

After All, It's Only Brain Surgery

Library of Congress
Cataloging in Publication Data
ISBN 1-56167-573-3

Library of Congress Card Catalog Number:
00-104103

Published by

Noble House

8019 Belair Road, Suite 10
Baltimore, Maryland 21236

Manufactured in the United States of America

Contents

Chapter 1
Can She Handle The Gore? 1
Chapter 2
Exactly Where Am I Going? 3
Chapter 3
Ship Surgeon On the Panama Line 11
Chapter 4
Uncle Sam Beckons 17
Chapter 5
Call Of The North Country 21
Chapter 6
Thomas I. Hoen 29
Chapter 7
Theodora and Timothy Getty 31
Chapter 8
We Are The Best, Aren't We? 41
Chapter 9
Wielders Of Axes And Knives 47
Chapter 10
Queen Square and Wimbledon 53
Chapter 11
Sir Geoffrey Jefferson 61
Chapter 12
In the Land of the Vikings 65
Chapter 13
Rubenstein The Great 69
Chapter 14
On My Own 75
Chapter 15
A Long Shot For Rosario Ricci 81
Chapter 16
Patricia Walks Again 87

Chapter 17
Subdural Hematoma —Trouble for All Ages 91
Chapter 18
The Toughest Night And The Longest Day 95
Chapter 19
 The Re-Creation of Linda Drake 101
Chapter 20
The Vegetable We Sent To Credemore
(The Robert Adler Story) 107
Chapter 21
Surprise, Surprise 111
Chapter 22
A Happy Mistake 115
Chapter 23
It's Hard To Kill A Newfoundlander
(Story Of Alice McNeil) 119
Chapter 24
Sorry, Doctor, You Made A Needless Trip
(Story of Dawn Skinner) 125
Chapter 25
Ah, Medical Politics—Is It Worth It? 129
Chapter 26
Bullets in the Brain 133
Chapter 27
Where Can a Guy Get Pronounced
Dead Around Here? 143
Chapter 28
As Good As The Old Egyptians 147
Chapter 29
The Mendizabel Story 151
Chapter 30
Sandy's Close Call 155
Chapter 31
Don't Give In To The System 159

Chapter 32
The Loaded Question 163
Chapter 33
Deborah Ribbe—Wonder Woman 169
Chapter 34
Coleen Colligan 173
Chapter 35
 Dead People Don't Breathe 177
Chapter 36
We Stand On Their Shoulders 181

ACKNOWLEDGMENTS

I owe much to two particular medical school classmates—Daniel Miller and Paul Zola for their lifelong friendship as well as specific advice in the preparation of this manuscript. Leonard Malis and Joseph Ransohoff, true giants of neurosurgery, were always "big brothers" on whom I could rely on for support, as well as my colleague Morris Loffman of Encino, California, who I thank for his warm friendship and shared experiences during our training and throughout our respective careers.

My editor, Alan C. Reese, has provided many valuable contributions and a certain forbearance that I could not have done without.

The recent untimely death of Johnnye Bradley, my publisher, friend, and source of inspiration, reminds me how tenuous life is. It is to her memory that this book is dedicated. Her hardworking, perpetually upbeat demeanor will never be forgotten by those of us who worked with her. I wish to honor her along with the memory of my deceased mentors.

INTRODUCTION

It's Only Brain Surgery

"Luke," we called him. His full name was Hans-Lukas Teuber, a World War II friend of Morris Boris Bender, my neurology chief at Bellevue. Dr. Bender helped inspire Luke to become a neurobiologist and eventually Luke developed a Ph.D. program at New York University. When I transferred to the neurosurgical department, Luke considered me the most loyal provider of human subjects for his neurobiology unit, and he greatly appreciated my efforts and always treated me in a kind and benevolent manner. I felt like an important member of his extended family. His Ph.D. trainees were, like himself, never under pressure, it seemed. Pure academia, what a peaceful existence!

One day in the late fifties, Luke informed me he of his decision to leave N.Y. U. to start up a neurobiology department at the Massachusetts Institute of Technology.

"I'm taking some of the crew along with me, Bill. Steve, Rita, maybe one or two others will be coming along—how about joining us? Take time off for a Ph.D. You're meant for it!" Luke was dead serious.

"I'd love to help figure out how the brain works," I replied, "but T.I. Hoen wouldn't go for it. He'd never let me back into the neurosurgical program if I left now."

Luke pressed on in his engaging way. "After all, Bill, what you're doing—it's only brain surgery!"

We both laughed. We also both realized I had made my final decision. I wouldn't leave N.Y. U. I muttered out loud as I left Luke's office, "Yeah, yeah, it's only brain surgery."

When I sat down to write this book, I knew I had my title as I thought back to this conversation with "Luke." Although this book is primarily a memoir, it represents a combination of professional pride mixed with a touch of literary vanity. At age twenty-one, I knew I would become some sort of neurologist, psychiatrist, or if I played my cards right, perhaps even a neurosurgeon.

To be a brain surgeon was the idealized goal of mine and neuropsychiatry was something to fall back on—a kind of fail-safe.

My six years of hospital training and thirty-four years of neurosurgical practice in Long Island has, in a way, left me gasping, "Wow, I actually did it!" My modest contributions to the science of cranial surgery seem far less important than some of the actual experiences with certain patients. These stories are what I long to share. This book is written with the general public in mind, more so than an academic study for my fellow professionals.

A contemporary of mine at Bellevue Hospital, William Nolan, wrote *The Making Of A Surgeon* (Random House), a crisp and lively book that can hardly be surpassed. The making of a neurosurgeon is quite well presented by Frank Vertosick in a volume called *When the Air Hits Your Brain*, (Norton). The stories in this volume span my entire career and focus on the care for trauma victims and the human stories behind them.

The fictionalized names include those whom I could not track down for permission to use the real ones. Eastern Nassau and Seaford General Hospital have been employed instead of the actual places. Dr. Reubenstein is an amalgam of several chiefs of neurosurgery I worked with in in my early years of practice. It has been my good fortune to be a part of the golden era of American medicine—the fifties, the sixties, and the seventies, prior to the excessive commercialization and intrusion of forces beyond the control of the medical profession.

William Herman Bloom
Bay Shore, NY
July 2000

Chapter 1

Can She Handle The Gore?

February 26, 1999: St. Ives, Australia

It was a dinner party for twelve, in this affluent suburb of Sydney, where I attended an international conference on radio-surgery. My wife, Barbara, originally from Johannesburg, South Africa, was thrilled with meeting her girlhood chum, Bernice. Bernice showed us much of Sydney and now arranged for her son to have us to his Sabbath family dinner.

While Bernice was busily chatting with Barbara, her twelve-year-old granddaughter, seated to my immediate left, suddenly asked, "What was the goriest situation you ever faced?"

All brain surgery is gory, at least to most people, I thought. What I need here is a quick story, and my thoughts went back to a small Long Island hospital emergency room,1965, and the case of the "dangling eyeballs."

A weird accident blinded a middle aged woman who clearly had alcohol on her breath. If she had been drunk she was sobered by the fact that she was totally and permanently blind.

"Oh, yes", I said, "I think it might be the woman whose eyeballs were hanging outside her lids by a narrow thread of tissue. Normally, the eye socket protects the eyeballs, but in this unusual car accident they popped out like grapes squeezed out of their skin." Though I spoke in a subdued voice, the nine-year-old brother half crawled over his sister's body to get in on the act. By this time, I had lowered my voice to a whisper to make sure the adults could not hear.

"Since there were no other serious injuries, the general surgeon snipped off the left eyeball while I did the same on the right. Then we stitched the lids together to prevent infection or fluid leakage."

Suddenly, it occurred to me that the room was dead silent. All the adults were staring at us even though they could not have heard a word. What could I possibly be telling these children to incur such rapt attention? The children appeared hypnotized—the adults were simply amazed by the spell I had cast over them.

The only fear we are born with is the fear of falling and of loud sounds. Children have no fear of blood or of dead bodies unless they have learned it from older people. If their mother is fearful at a funeral, they will be fearful as well. I closely monitored the reactions of the two children as I told the story and knew they could take it.

In my career, I have known queasiness. The day that I had to skin my cadaver in anatomy lab in medical school, the day I saw my first surgical operation, the day I undertook to assist at surgery, and the time I did my first surgical procedure alone. Isn't all life associated with conquering one's fears and misgivings? We climb the ladder of courage rung by rung, each step adding to our self assurance, as we feel and test our way through the demands of our profession, as well as the tempests of life itself.

The children suffered no loss of appetite. They were obviously enthused by my little story, feeling I was treating them as grown-ups.

Certainly I would not have told the story to the adults. It would have been unseemly, vulgar, and obviously in poor taste. Besides they couldn't have taken it like my young audience.

Chapter 2

Exactly Where Am I Going?

In my youth I studied the mind, the brain, the nervous system—humans and animals—with great verve and enormous curiosity. Career-wise it didn't lead in any particular direction. Psychology for two years and a semester of comparative neurology of the vertebrates where I dissected the brains of a dogfish shark, a sheep, and a cat were all of equal interest. After all, wouldn't it all come together? Wasn't psychology and neurology part of the same system?

Medical school clearly shaped my decision. Psychology was out, including psychiatry—not scientific enough, I thought. If psychiatry worked, it was not because of any inherent scientific principles but due to the innate human, and humane, qualities of the psychiatrist. There was, despite its fascination, an off-turning mumbo-jumbo aspect of psychiatry. As a medical student, I would anguish over choosing between neurology and neurosurgery. With neurology I knew I would rise to the top. With neurosurgery I wasn't so sure. I leaned rapidly toward neurology, knowing, of course, that neuropsychiatry was a linkage that could not be avoided. I would be a neurologist and force myself to learn psychiatry, that was it!

Then I encountered neurosurgery in the form of the most dynamic man on the University of Buffalo Medical faculty—Dr. Wallace Hamby, the Professor of Neurosurgery. He looked and acted like a movie actor, always on center stage. He had all the requisite characteristics—best dressed, best orator, most skillful artist, letter-perfect, in the operating room or out. In the operating room, he was slick and sure of himself. Everyone thought he was the next thing to God. He never failed. His respect was well deserved, my concept of the perfect man. Actually I was intimidated by him at first, but eventually reached him on a person-to person basis. It took me two years. One needed to be completely sure of one's self and behave that way before the watching world. There's where I wavered. How did Dr. Hamby get to be that way? Doesn't he have imperfections? As an artist, he was superb and actually had one of his oil paintings hanging in the Saturn Club, one of Buffalo's most exclusive clubs. Even if I had Hamby's talent, could I ever carry it off like he does?

In the meantime there was William Beswick. Hamby was the chief, and Beswick was the junior in the two-man department on the faculty. Carl Graf, Hamby's first trainee, would soon reach faculty status. I related well with Beswick. Unlike Hamby, he was warm, reachable, ready to explain anything and everything— my kind of guy. I followed Dr. Beswick around the Millard Fillmore Hospital, where he did most of his surgery. It was Beswick, not Hamby that made me feel that, yes, little old me would be able to handle such awe-inspiring responsibility.

Yet it was Hamby that had the power, and it was Hamby with whom I had to deal ultimately. As a twenty-one-year-old junior medical student, I made my decision, unique in my class, to try to become a neurosurgeon. Dan Miller, the classmate who edited our school yearbook referred to me as the "nervous surgeon," realizing my personal insecurity regarding my stated objective. He also called me "Dr. Beswick's shadow" and was right on target there as well.

Eventually, on the advice of William German, head of the Yale Neurosurgical Department and Secretary of the American Board of Neurologic Surgery, I would opt for a surgical internship at the Buffalo General Hospital. First, it was necessary to get my medical diploma.

Being a good student did not guarantee that one would finish school automatically. In those days, it was important not to displease or antagonize a member of the faculty. One of our brightest classmates was expelled, supposedly for giving information on an exam, but more likely because his arrogance was not appreciated by someone on the faculty. Membership in the medical profession was a little like getting into a fancy club, where one blackball keeps you out forever.

My own approach was to remain servile, almost timid, in this regard, and I recall one example that I cannot ever forget: As a senior student assigned to pediatrics, I participated in a minor way in the first child operated on at the Buffalo Children's Hospital for congenital heart problems. The first "blue-baby" operation in the USA was done at the Boston Children's Hospital. Our faculty found a septal defect in a child and planned surgery.

I finally achieved a modicum of power in that I could now give orders to a junior student, a fraternity brother of mine.

"What was the blood pressure in the legs compared to the arms?" I asked after telling him to check both.

"The leg pressure was lower than the arm pressure," he replied.

"That means coarctation of the aorta," I said, referring to a constriction of the main artery leading out of the heart. The book says congenital heart problems can be multiple. I recorded all this on the chart but no one apparently paid attention.

I was careful, though, to record "possible coexisting coarctation" in my desire not to displease or even embarrass any of the faculty, even though I was quite sure they were two separate problems.

The big day came, and the highly-touted operation took place with at least twenty onlookers. I stood among them wondering what would happen when the bigwigs discovered the second problem.

Sure enough there came a pause when the surgeons, previously talking aloud, began to whisper. The pediatrics professor turned to the audience and asked straight out: "Anyone here diagnose coarctation of the aorta?"

My hand went up, a bit weakly, since the pediatrics professor had been scowling at me for one reason or another for quite some time.

The scowl again covered his face as though to say, "Oh, oh, you again." My moment of glory eluded me. I retreated into myself, faded away into nothingness.

Never did I mention this moment. Never did I consider becoming a cardiac surgeon, though this story could have helped launch me. I didn't even tell it to my best friends, family or anyone. The glare on Professor Rubin's face seemed to erase me from the operating room, and for a time, at least, from the face of the earth.

How would a delicate, sensitive person, like myself, so easily intimidated by Professor Rubin, ever even think of brain surgery?

I thought about it for about ten years before I had an answer: While others think they're twice as good as they really are I was different—I thought I was only half as good as I was. It was a self-image problem.

Alone one day with Professor Hamby, I asked him, at the proper moment, if he would take me on as a trainee.

"First, let's send you to "Pappy" Wechsler for a year," he replied. "He's the best neurologist in the country." Pappy was Hamby's affectionate term for the distinguished New York neurologist, Israel Wechsler.

After my internship, I did apply and became a resident with Dr. Wechsler at the Mount Sinai Hospital in New York City. I also interviewed at Montefiore Hospital with Houston Merritt, co-discoverer of dilantin, now a standard drug used in the treatment of epilepsy. Merritt was the up-and-coming neurologist who would soon supersede Wechsler as America's preeminent neurologist. However, Merritt was moving to Columbia

Presbyterian Medical Center to take over as chairman of that department. He couldn't accept me at Columbia for at least another year. That made my decision to proceed with Wechsler.

After my surgical internship, I drove to New York City with my French girlfriend Francois Jacobs, bid her farewell as we decided to break up, and entered the Mt. Sinai Hospital to begin a rather exciting year as assistant resident with one of the giants of American neurology, author of the standard *Textbook of Clinical Neurology*.

My relationship with Wechsler couldn't have been better. He spotted me as a potential academic, had me present a paper at the New York Academy of Medicine, and took me with him to the prestigious American Neurological Association meeting that year.

The senior resident in neurosurgery, Leonard Malis, made a profound impression on me, spouting information like an inexhaustible fountain of knowledge. I learned as much from Leonard as all the senior people put together—medical, surgical, neurological, worldly stuff that I soaked up appreciatively.

One day he asked me, on behalf of the neurosurgical department chief, Ira Cohen, if I would join their group. That meant crossing the Rubicon since the two were really separate disciplines. I felt I had the skills for neurosurgery and that my confidence would grow. I was then only 23-years-old. It was a moment that changed my life. Someone in a position that counts finally invited me to become a neurosurgeon. I decided to remain in New York City. No longer would I worry whether Wallace Hamby would accept me even though it occurred to me that he never answered my original request to be his trainee. I decided not to push the point, and as I got to like New York better than Buffalo, I never wrote him how things were going.

Israel Wechsler was a bit displeased at first but accepted my decision. Since it was an approved residency I felt I finally belonged and could see my way clear for the future, hitherto uncertain, it would be neurosurgery for sure! Easy decision—

tough career. Lots of work, night and day, with much self-sacrifice. The new career would not be easy, and I knew it well.

Paul Teng was said to have been the most brilliant student ever to have matriculated at the Medical School in Chungking, China. Speaking English and German fluently he came to New York, first to Columbia University where he wrote some of the original articles with Dr. Meleney on bacitracin, then a new wonder drug. Paul was the junior resident in neurosurgery at Mt. Sinai. It was a distinct honor to be next in line after Leonard Malis and Paul Teng. Prior to Leonard, there had been Aaron Beller, who became the first neurosurgeon of the newly formed State of Israel.

People often ask me how it was performing my first brain operation. It was somewhat like flying a plane. You have an instructor who flies with you and guides you during your training program, and he then turns you loose on your own. He chooses the right psychological moment to have you do a few easy take-offs and landings. Then he lets himself out of the plane very, very casually and gently says, "You can handle it. Why don't you just take her for a run around the field, and I'll be right here."

That is how my flying instructor ever so gently released me for my first brief solo flight. And that is the way the attending surgeon, having guided me, turned the controls—in this case the surgical instruments—over to me. There is no one special solo moment in surgery as in flying. To be sure, the surgeon can stand a few feet away, and you feel just a little more secure perhaps than when you are up there a couple of thousand feet in the air and alone. While flying is an all-or-nothing phenomenon, when one solos in surgery, it is a progression of a number of operating room experiences—first, closing the wound, then opening the next one, then raising the bone flap, then delicately opening the dural membrane over the brain with a knife; perhaps handling the electrocautery apparatus to stop bleeding. The next step might be cauterizing the surface of the brain, then gently entering it, handling delicate forceps and little threaded sponges and squirting saline over the brain tissue to keep its moisture content up, pressing bone wax with the thumb against the edges of the bone, as Victor Horsley did back in the 1890s.

After leaving residency and fellowship and entering the private practice world, one continues to grow. By this time, the acquired skills are sufficient to keep you going.

Chapter 3

Ship Surgeon On the Panama Line

Being a good doctor was always important to me. Israel Wechsler would always stress that "you can't be a good neurologist unless you are a good doctor first." One can, for example, be a slick and skillful surgical technician and still be an uncaring, and therefore, a poor doctor, in my estimation. I've run into a few of those in my time.

There is nothing like experience to whip a young doctor into shape, and at the same time, test his mettle, his ability to adapt, and his wisdom, assuming he has any to begin with. Looking back to January 1950, it was my first unsupervised experience as a responsible physician. I was just six months out of my internship, during my neurology residency in New York when I was allowed a two week vacation.

Just imagine it—getting paid $160 (after taxes) for being on a cruise ship, instead of paying passage. Free food, free laundry service! Five paying passengers at my table—the doctor's table—to socialize with, much like the captain's table or the pursar's table.

A New York urologist, Dr. Lowsley, had recruited me to be ship's doctor for a single two week cruise on the Panama Line. The Caribbean Sea in January would offer a welcome sight. Captain Hirsch of the SS Panama had me make ship rounds with himself and the chief engineer every day as well as having me schedule office hours twice daily totaling one-and-one-half hours. The rest of the day I had to myself.

Of course, I would be responsible for the health of the crew and ninety passengers. I was about to reach my 24th birthday and wet behind the ears as a practicing doctor. Undeniably, it would be a great challenge.

I began to check over the materials and drugs in the doctor's office, which included a table for minor surgery.

What if, while at sea, one of the group needs gall bladder surgery or ruptures an ovarian cyst? I began to worry. I was good at removing hemorrhoids, tonsils, and maybe an inflamed appendix if it wasn't too complicated, but what about a perforated ulcer or a chest wound? There were lots of things that could happen that I could not handle alone!

"Don't worry," Captain Hirsch assured me. "If it's beyond your scope we'll just radio the Coast Guard for a rescue boat or call in for a helicopter evacuation."

That helped me to feel a little less anxious. Then, while reviewing the passenger roster, my heart leaped as I saw the name Dr. Sengstack. I tracked him down at once! He turned out to be twice my age, an experienced general surgeon from Huntington, Long Island.

"Don't worry," said Dr. Sengstack, as he saw the anxiety on my face. "I'm here to enjoy the trip, but if you should need any help, I'll be ready to assist you."

The five day trip from New York to Cristobel, the Canal Zone port, went smoothly in all respects—good weather, no serious medical problems, and delightful shipboard companions. One was an engineer who, fifty years previously, helped to build the canal. Then there was Mrs. Papp, a mover and a shaker for social events. Two unattached females were placed at the doctor's table. The whole situation began to resemble a regular "Love-Boat" scenario. There was a British geologist, quite handsome, fortyish, and a thirty-two-year old female interior decorator from Queens, New York who were "hitting it off" quite nicely.

Several Canal Zone employees befriended me, offering to put me up for the four-day stopover in Panama. One of them loaned me his car for the first two days and then hosted me on the Pacific side of the Zone.

Each day in the Zone was eventful. One day I swam in the waters of the Atlantic in the morning and in that of the Pacific in the afternoon. Crossing the "transcontinental" highway that connected the two I decided to pull off the road, park, and take a stroll in the jungle. Except for Tarzan movies I'd never seen a jungle. It was not to my liking, being unwalkable, and totally impassable. No wonder Christopher Columbus didn't venture to the Pacific side. Balboa had his troubles and barely made it years later.

In a night club in Panama City where my host, a fireman, had taken me, I was jitterbugging away when I spotted a man on the dance floor a few years older than myself and a few notches higher on the scale of smooth dancers. I judged him to be a Panamanian, most likely, certainly a Latin, not realizing our paths would soon cross.

Next day, I was given a tour of Panama City by Red Smith, an American radio broadcaster, and a tour of the Gorgas General Hospital by a Dr. Arias. Smith showed me the homes of five or six wealthy families that controlled both the government and the economy. They lived near the statue of Balboa. One of the families was named Arias, and Dr. Arias was one of its members.

Another member was the twenty-seven-year-old Roberto Arias, the gifted dancer I had encountered. He was the nephew of Arnulfo Arias, who had recently become president of this small nation.

Roberto, also called Tito, was a passenger on the SS Panama for our return voyage and was reluctantly on his way to Washington as a diplomat.

"My Uncle Arnulfo wouldn't let me go where I preferred—Paris or Madrid, and insisted I get experience in the United States first," he told me. There had just been a revolution in

Panama, where Roberto played an active part in getting his uncle placed into the presidential chair. Tito knew all about weapons, including Molotov Cocktails. When asked how he learned to make and throw Molotov Cocktails he said, "We practiced in Costa Rica until the time was ripe."

Years later, I read about Tito marrying Margot Fonteyn, the noted ballerina, and wondered how they looked together on the dance floor. Of course, this was before Tito was tragically rendered paraplegic by a would-be assassin's bullet shattering his spinal cord.

Besides the company of Tito Arias, the return voyage was more exciting medically as well. There were two middle-aged women who never came to the dining room, both being bedridden. One called me to her stateroom the first day, plagued by arthritis all over her body. I discovered one of her big toes to be swollen at its base. It looked like a case of gout. I ran back to my medicine cabinet and to my delight we had colchicine. I grabbed a few tiny tablets and consulted my older buddy, Dr. Sengstack. We discussed proper dosage, and I returned to the patient's stateroom to administer the healing medication.

Within a day or two she was greatly improved and able to walk. It was a medical triumph at sea. The lady actually had two separate forms of arthritis, but it was the acute gouty variety that needed treatment. She had consulted with several Costa Rican doctors but none had picked up the gout, obscured as it was by her degenerative arthritis.

Mrs. Bigbux, the other disabled lady, didn't call me until after dinner the night before we pulled in to New York City. She told me her story as I sat in a chair adjacent to her bed.

"I have leukemia and my life span is limited, so to speak. My husband allowed me to go on a fun trip to enjoy myself. I would have been on one of the other ships back to New York, but I collapsed and had to have a blood transfusion!"

She had my full attention and sympathy and I acceded to her two requests. I would guarantee her medicine to put her asleep, and I would wheel her off the boat in her wheelchair at eight a.m. the following morning.

Examining her lungs I leaned over her with a stethoscope when suddenly, she pulled me down on top of her. From face to pelvis we were in intimate contact, in what, to a totally objective observer, might be easily misconstrued as the "missionary position" or certainly something more than an innocent medical examination.

It happened so fast I thought, at first, I might have lost my balance. There was a flurry of mutual apologies, and soon I realized what had happened.

"Oh, I feel so terrible, doctor. I have a son your age in medical school. I'm really a good woman with a good family. Please don't think badly of me." She pointed excitedly at the picture of her beautiful family.

"Don't feel bad," I reassured her. I left her bedside to get the paraldehyde.

I'm a fun-loving guy, but I hadn't signed on to provide stud service for ailing and lonely matrons. Be cordial, be a good doctor, try to understand her position, I told myself. A wealthy woman under a death sentence may deserve a stud, but I was only going to be her doctor.

As I reentered the stateroom with my syringe containing the paraldehyde, I had an appreciative and compliant patient, still concerned about what I thought about her.

I helped roll her over onto her belly then lifted her nightie, exposing her buttocks. I rubbed each with alcohol, delivered the medicine to her gluteal muscles, just enough to put her asleep but not so much that she would be excessively groggy in the morning. Then I spent another ten minutes with her telling her what a wonderful a woman she must be, how lucky her children were to have her.

With my extra dose of tender loving care completed and with the medicine beginning to take effect, I told her I would be back to awaken her and personally wheel her off the boat in

New York Harbor.

And I did exactly that. In a wheelchair covered with a blanket, the now wide-awake gracious lady was wheeled by me to her waiting husband, a wealthy Midwestern industrialist. Thinking I was the porter, he slipped me a twenty dollar bill. I started to give the tip back saying, "I'm not the porter, sir. I'm only the ship's doctor."

Suddenly, I changed my mind and left abruptly. I was no longer needed. "I'm worth at least as much as the porter," I told myself and slipped the twenty bucks into my pocket.

Chapter 4

Uncle Sam Beckons

In 1950, there were less than three hundred board certified neurosurgeons in the country, and I felt rather lucky to be in a training program, surrounded by hard-working and competent people.

Alas, after only three and a half months on the neurosurgical service, a letter arrived summoning me to military duty as a naval medical officer on loan to the army. The Korean War was on, and I was given two weeks to report for duty in San Antonio, Texas. The navy loaned five hundred doctors to the army, and I was one of them.

Quick farewell parties were held including one where Diane, my "best girl," an adorable student nurse at the hospital, and four or five other ex-girlfriends were all present, along with my closest male friends. The neurology and neurosurgical departments held a late afternoon party with pastrami sandwiches and wine, presenting me with one of Harvey Cushing's books on brain tumors. All present signed the book, wishing me well in military service.

The Korean War was in full swing and the United States Army, having discharged their medical officers at the end of World War II, had no reserves to draw from, unlike the Navy. After what was called "unification of the services," the Army tapped the Navy for 500 of their reserve doctors, since they were the only service that had them. I was included in this group.

We newly-arrived military doctors were given a greatly condensed course at Fort Sam Houston, in San Antonio, Texas. From there I was assigned to William Beaumont Army Hospital in El Paso. The Navy doctors were much appreciated and well-received. I was fortunate enough to be made Chief of Neurosurgery at the hospital for a short period of time. Except for Warren Porter, a neurologist, there were no other staff members who had any training in clinical neuroscience.

After a time, the Army replaced their own dispensary officers at Fort Bliss with Navy men. I was included in this gradual change. Thereafter, our medical duties became somewhat boring.

I may have fallen in love with life itself during this period of relative relaxation. Unlike my civilian past, I was no longer driving myself to accomplish things. One friend, Tom Lewis, introduced me to Mexico, bullfighting and Spanish culture. John Daniels, a young intern at the hospital about my age, studied conversational Spanish with me and, after each class, we would cross the Rio Grande into Juarez to practice our new language in the real setting. This included restaurants, where we would marvel at the low price of sirloin steak (sometimes under a dollar) and a whiskey sour (only fifteen cents). Naturally, all this was conducted in Spanish.

Eventually, it was back to the Navy at San Diego's naval hospital, where the commanding officer, Captain Morrison, importuned me to consider joining the regular Navy. He realized my concerns about the standards of military medicine, and assured me that the Navy would see to it that the best medical care would be available to its personnel. The life of a Navy medical officer would match, in its totality, that of a civilian position, Captain Morrison assured me. When it came to hobbies and free time, the Navy doctors might even be better off.

I considered the transfer to regular Navy very seriously, particularly since my own immediate superior, Commander Richard Garrity, was a superb neurosurgeon who had trained at the Massachusetts General Hospital, and could handle neurosurgical and related problems very well. To me, Dr. Garrity was living proof of the new breed of specialists serving in the regular Navy.

Leo Davidoff had become Chief of Neurosurgery at Mt. Sinai. I met him on a short leave, and he promised to integrate me into his program whenever I finished military service. Having had a taste of the realities of life, including good living as an officer, I realized I had been shielded by the halls of academia in my earlier years.

My last several months were served at the Oakland Naval Hospital, when I finally decided to abandon thoughts of a military career. Yet, I was rather uncertain about Dr. Davidoff, inasmuch as he was reputed to be a taskmaster. He was Harvey Cushing's best pupil, perhaps, but he was as tough as his old boss or perhaps a shade tougher on his resident trainees. The latter all required psychiatric assistance, according to one rumor, but that likely was an exaggeration.

Procrastination set in right up until the time of my discharge. Something in me did not wish to face the intensity of training, a virtual rat race. I packed my bags, studied some maps, and set out to cross the country alone. I needed time to think and sort myself out. Perhaps a fresh breeze would sweep away the cobwebs in my confused mind.

Chapter 5

Call Of The North Country

After two years as a navy doctor during The Korean War, I became a neurosurgical dropout. Even in the old days some of us needed to find ourselves. First it was home that I craved, that ever-forgiving welcome I received from my parents in Granville, my home town. Rest, no rat-race. Then a change of pace. One available job was in Nepal, halfway around the world, courtesy of the World Medical Association where I would be a public health officer. I was told transportation would involve riding elephants within the remote provinces. I gave up the idea as too exotic and uncomfortable, too far away–I could return home only every eighteen months!

Eventually, I settled in the nearby community of Glens Falls as a house officer in the local hospital, for a four month period. Mike Bril, my Serbian roommate, told me of the opportunity at Lake Luzerne, a nearby village, township and mountain lake. The community was desperate to have their own physician. Some of the other house doctors were grasping opportunities in general practice in villages of northeastern New York State. Les Stanton, town supervisor of Lake Luzerne was quite specific on the telephone: "I personally own the local theater and will turn the popcorn store adjoining it into a doctor's office. The local Lion's Club will build partitions to your specifications and construct your office within ten days. You'll get the office rent-free for the first year and a salary of $1,000 for the year as Town Physician. Another $1,000 is yours as School Physician of the Luzerne-Hadley School System and $300 as our public health officer. We need you badly."

"I'll take it," I replied. "Be there in an hour to discuss it." How nice to be so needed, so wanted.

The village bordered a half-mile diameter lake, circumscribed by small mountains and colonies of cottages. Four dude-ranches nearby enabled city folks to pretend they were cowboys of the Wild West and some of the ranch hands were actually western cowhands who led groups on gentle horse rides. They themselves would participate in Friday night rodeos, thrilling the paying guests with their not-so-gentle performances.

Back in the early 1950s when office visits were $3.00 and house calls $4.00, the financial stimulus was appealing and as a young doctor in my twenties I had decided halfway through Les Stanton's phone call that the offer was irresistible. Now, four days later, I visited the village, my office half completed. The local druggist handed me a medical bag filled with drugs and a stethoscope and gave me names and addresses of three people who wanted house calls "as soon as the new doctor starts."

"And how did you figure which drugs I would need?" I asked.

The druggist didn't hesitate with his answer: "Look here, we've got regular digitalis for the heart patients, the little white tablets are phenobarbital, there's APC with codeine, and some morphine, and penicillin. There's also a few syringes."

"What are the purple pills for?" I asked.

"They are just ordinary aspirin pills," he replied. "You don't have to tell them it's aspirin. It's always good to be mysterious on occasion."

"Thanks for teaching me the art of medical practice." I was off to the first patient. My career as a practicing doctor was launched, it seemed. My very first patient turned out to have acute appendicitis, and I phoned the rescue squad ambulance to take the young man off to the Glens Falls Hospital Emergency

Room. The second had a septic sore throat with a fever of 103 degrees according to the thermometer the pharmacist had slipped into my bag. Time for a penicillin injection. The third had been lying in bed since a heart attack the night before. After injecting morphine, I called the rescue squad again.

On my drive back to the center of the village, I wondered what would have happened to each of these sick patients if I weren't on the scene. The happy druggist greeted me with the news that the community heard I had begun practice and five more people had called in for house calls. It was now 5 p.m. and having put nearly a full day at the Glens Falls Hospital, I foresaw a very full evening as I started out on what would be my fourth house call. There was no chance at all that I wasn't needed in Lake Luzerne. My father had hoped I would do all this in Granville, but fathers are all that way—they want you nearby. Too many folks in my hometown knew me as a kid. It was better to be forty miles away where the whole town would respect me as a full-fledged adult.

Soon, I leased a place on the lake where I could fish, swim, and take up water skiing. One of the dude-ranches made me official doctor for the Friday night rodeos. I joined the Dog-and-Pup Club and took up hunting. Ray Moffitt, my medical school roommate visited and almost joined me in this remote but blissful life-style.

One house call fourteen miles north turned out to be a wealthy recluse who was astounded to have a doctor in his house twenty minutes after making the phone call. "I'll pay you for the call, Doctor, I just wanted to get to know you and also to make sure you'll come when I really need you." The elderly man owned racehorses, never worked in his life, born to inherited wealth. He became a true patient soon thereafter, one of the many interesting local residents who was thrilled by my availability.

Another time, I got a call from old man Reeves' house. His wife and three children were with him. I arrived and on the front porch, it looked like old man Reeves had chopped two full cords of wood—not bad for an eighty-five-year-old guy. People up in the Adirondacks that put in a good 10 or 12 hours a day of hard physical work, seem to remain in good shape well into their seventies and eighties and old man Reeves was no exception. I wondered how long it had taken for him to chop all that wood, and thought he couldn't be too sick.

Oh, bless my soul, I was entirely wrong! Reeves was in deep trouble. He had had this progressive swallowing problem, a lumpy feeling in his stomach, weight loss, and then regurgitating some blood, he also had black stools, a sign of upper intestinal or stomach bleeding. I diagnosed stomach cancer and, of course, the family wanted to know what could be done.

"We could admit him to the Glens Fall's Hospital and have one of our four surgeons look him over," I suggested. Then they wanted to know how long people can live with this and we talked about the surgery, removal of stomach, and the troubles that go along with all of this. I was as honest and straight as I could be, as usual.

Finally Reeves' son spoke up and said, "You know, doc, Pop has never been sick in his life."

"I'm not surprised," I replied. "Anybody that can cut two cord of wood by the end of October, has got to be in good shape, but that doesn't change the outlook." They finally talked it over another five minutes or so and came up with their decision.

"Well, doc, you don't mind if he just dies at home do you?"

"Of course not," I replied. "Why would I mind? It's your decision to make, and you've made it."

"But, doc, if you were Pop, let's say, and you had the cancer yourself, you know, what would have been your decision?"

"Exactly the same."

Work hard, play hard—that became my credo. The play included stream and lake fishing, canoeing, dear hunting (female relationships, very carefully selected and always out-of-town), and studying aviation. After getting my pilot's license I bought a 4-place Stinson Aircraft, useful for getting to New York City, Boston and, on one occasion, Florida.

Joining the Saratoga unit of the Civil Air Patrol as a pilot, I flew it's first official mission. We landed at the Air Force base at Rome, New York, to procure uniforms for our newly-founded squadron.

One day, one of my patients, Harriet Clemons, offered me her backyard as a landing field. It was nearly half of a mile long including the approaches. There was only one "pothole." I marked this with a tall wooden plank, as a danger point. Then I drove my car, going 50 miles an hour, over my single runway to determine whether I could land and take off properly. It seemed smooth enough to bring in the Bluebird (the name of my plane) for a landing in its new home. How convenient! I could drive to the plane, get out of my car and be aloft within ten minutes of leaving my house.

I asked Harriet what the lease would amount to, now that I converted her backyard into my private little airport.

"Nothing at all, Dr. Bloom. After all, it's only a field. I don't mow the grass and your little airplane looks so cute there." Harriet would not accept a single penny. Finally, she let me treat her to a couple of free office visits.

There's something about a small community that I like. Harriet Clemons was just an example. She and others like her understood about giving and taking and, most of all, sharing.

I would often fly over Lake George and explore the Adirondack Mountains with its many lakes and peaks. Then, I would land back at my private "airport," hop in my car and get to work.

I kept fishing gear in the car's trunk for trout fishing in the little streams, but often would take out a rowboat on Lake Luzerne in the early morning to catch some sunfish to fry for breakfast. Then, I would swim to the nearby water-ski school and water-ski around the little lake.

When I worked, I would gab with the locals on the way and

became their friends. Payment was often in materials. Those who couldn't afford the $3.00 office visit fees would bring me garden vegetables, rhubarb, salad materials and even recently baked pies.

One patient came in with a two-foot long northern pike, just caught under the ice in winter-time. I made at least two meals out of it! A restaurant owner didn't have money for the two weeks he spent in the hospital from his heart attack and asked if I would accept eight dinners in his little place of business. Of course, the answer was yes. He made great fried clams, I recall.

Once a hunter, his bank account low, offered me the opportunity to shoot a deer, and I accepted. This was probably a mistake, but I only realized it twenty years later, long after I had left the area to became a neurosurgeon. I recall passing through the tiny adjacent village of Stony Creek. I parked my car in front of the Stony Creek Hotel, entered the bar and ordered a tap beer. I had been driving quite awhile and I wondered if there just might be any old familiar faces. Within a few minutes, a bewhiskered old geezer turned to me and said, "Hey, aren't you Doc Bloom?" At first, I didn't recognize him.

"Yeah, that's me," I replied.

"Well, you are one miserable son of a bitch!" All my alerting mechanisms were in force. Surely the man was joking. I waited for a smile to appear on his face, but it obviously wasn't coming.

"What's this all about?" I asked, my face becoming very serious. I had never been in a barroom brawl. Although this old guy would be no problem, it wasn't in keeping with my medical career to be involved in fisticuffs.

The geezer continued, "You don't seem to remember that we went deer hunting one morning, and I told you that I would drive a deer in front of you. You and another guy were supposed to be waiting for the deer and shoot him. You do remember, don't you? You ain't senile yet. I comes by and looks at the two of you and you're both sleeping. The deer went right by. What in the hell's wrong with you guys. You both total idiots?"

"Oh", I lied, "it's all a vague memory but you have to remember I was up half the night with a couple of sick people and I was exhausted. I'm so terribly sorry, I just couldn't stay awake. Being a doctor has certain obligations".

"What about the other guy? He's no doctor. He wasn't up all night".

"You'll have to speak to him directly", I replied. "I can only speak for myself. But again, I have to apologize. I would have shot the deer if I had been awake. It's really hard to stay awake early in the morning when you've been up till three a.m."

The geezer was unrelenting. I gulped the last of my beer and left.

I must confess I had forgotten both the man and the incident. But, it finally came to me clearly. The main reason I fell asleep was that I never had shot and killed an animal in my life. The hiking and the great outdoors were what I craved. I hadn't developed my killer instinct. I didn't really want to shoot the deer in the first place! Obviously, I had been imprudent accepting the hunter's invitation and should have told him simply to forget about the money he owed me.

Eventually, Paul Zola talked me out of this sybaritic existence and persuaded me to pursue my original goal, that of becoming a neurosurgeon. Paul didn't have to convince me. Deep down I wanted to be the best I could be. I picked up the phone and called Morris B. Bender, a neurologist who had training programs at Bellevue-NYU and at Mt. Sinai. He offered me a job at Bellevue Hospital. I would proceed to my fail-safe neurology, and then go on to neurosurgery. My two and a half years as a general practitioner, in retrospect, made me a better doctor and a more mature man.

Chapter 6

Thomas I. Hoen

The Professor and Chairman of the Department of Neurosurgery at New York University was a tall, broad-shouldered man whose appearance connoted strength and dignity simultaneously. T. I. was a man to be reckoned with. He was born in Baltimore and educated at the John Hopkins Medical School where the famed Walter Dandy carried out his superb operative neurosurgery. T. I. learned by watching Dr. Dandy and later absorbed and utilized many of his techniques in the operating room. His formal neurosurgical training was with Harvey Cushing in Boston.

Before arriving on the New York scene, Hoen worked in Montreal, married a local girl from a prominent family and was, in essence, a sort of super-resident in the training of junior neurosurgeons, working with the director, Wilder Penfield, the founder of the Montreal Neurologic Institute. Penfield, a brilliant neurophysiologist and expert neuropathologist, was best-known for introducing epilepsy surgery. The Montreal Neurologic Institute was to become the outstanding center for this type of procedure.

In short, Tom Hoen trained with the world's best—Dandy, Cushing, and Penfield and had much to offer when he arrived in New York. Waspish, patrician, and dynamic in every way, Hoen was highly regarded as a skillful technician. At his best, he was incomparable. Agreeing with me on this matter was none other than Sir Geoffrey Jefferson, admittedly a good friend of Hoen's, but an honest and distinguished man who called things as he saw them. Hoen, in my estimation, was always adequate for the task, but he seemed at his best when visitors were watching.

In his home in Cedarhurst, Long Island, Hoen kept a workshop in his basement, where he designed and tested new surgical instruments. At the end of my training, he gave me a Hoen retractor as a gift and I used it throughout my career for my disc operations.

Hoen was tough and talented, but not really anxious to prove to the world how worthy he was, unlike most of his neurosurgical colleagues. He was responsible for training two neurosurgeons per year, and he appeared to pick his men reasonably carefully. He was not afraid of firing them if they failed to meet his standards. If any trainee seemed to be in the field for the money, he knew how to make things tough for them and would either fire them outright or force them to leave in a more subtle fashion. I am happy to say that I gave my all to my training, for I was determined to be one of those whom T. I. regarded as fit in all respects.

Between Mt. Sinai and the N.Y.U. service at Bellevue Hospital, I put in a good five years of training, first in neurology and then in neurosurgery. The experience, as a general practioner, made a better doctor out of me. All too many of my colleagues can be slick and smooth in the operating room, yet remain poor doctors, often unwilling to spend sufficient time with patients and families.

While Mt. Sinai tended to oversupervise, Bellevue gave us a heavy burden of responsibility. Between the two, I achieved great balance. It served me well in my career to have trained at both institutions.

Chapter 7

Theodora and Timothy Getty

It was the summer of 1958 as I walked the seven blocks from Bellevue Hospital to the University Hospital of NYU, at 20th Street and 2nd Avenue. As I approached the entrance, realizing I had only another year to complete my training, I decided to climb the stairs to the tenth floor since there was never sufficient time for sport or exercise.

Neurosurgical training was not for mentally, physically, or morally weak individuals, I thought. T.I. Hoen, my boss, had fired two of his trainees in the preceding four years, one of them as late as the last three months of his residency.

When I first began my assignment at University Hospital, I stayed on call night and day for two weeks. Finally I gently hinted to T.I. that it might be nice to have a day off.

Always ready to intimidate his resident trainee, T.I. responded, "I remember when I first went to work for Harvey Cushing. There was no such thing as time off. It was six weeks before I finally sneaked off to the opera."

T.I. was, of course, referring to 1929. For a brief moment, I was about to mention that we were now in 1958, when something inside me told me it would be prudent to keep that fact to myself.

Puffing somewhat, I arrived at what I termed the "Getty Suite," two hospital rooms, completely private and interconnected. I stood silently for a minute, catching my breath before knocking. The door opened and I was greeted by a stately, calm and rather striking woman of patrician bearing.

"Sit down for a few minutes and let's talk about your taps," Theodora said.

I had started several days earlier on a series of 30 methotrexate injections for her son, Timothy, who occupied the adjacent room. Fifteen were to be made into the spinal canal and 15 directly into a burr hole where the needle tip would be in a cystic pool of fluid within the intracranial cavity. It was felt that this was the best chance for eradicating the rest of Timothy's brain tumor. Known as a craniopharyngioma, this so-called "benign tumor," can be exceedingly troublesome, causing blindness and often a fatal outcome.

This eleven-year-old lad had undergone two operations. The first had been done at age five, by Dr. J. Lawrence Poole, at The Neurologic Institute, Columbia Presbyterian Hospital. Five and a half years later, Timothy had to be rushed back to the hospital. He was deteriorating. Dr. Poole was out of the country. Theodora was told one of the other surgeons on the staff would be able to take over the surgery. She had met and been favorably impressed by T.I. Hoen and felt that if Timothy should again need surgical care, T.I. would do the surgery.

I wasn't there, but I can just picture the hospital officials at The Neurologic Institute and the hand-wringing that went on at that point.

"But Dr. Hoen is not a member of our staff," she was told.

Theodora replied, "in that case, call me a cab and let's bring Timothy downstairs and I shall take him to University Hospital at NYU, since T.I. Hoen is on the staff there, and he is the one who is going to do the surgery."

There had to have been a rapid flurry of phone calls because soon thereafter a smiling official notified Theodora that the problem was totally solved and T.I. Hoen was now given temporary surgical privileges so that he could carry out the procedure at the Neurologic Institute.

Theodora realized that time was of the essence. She reached T.I. by phone and summoned him immediately to the Neurological Institute, as Timothy was deteriorating fairly rapidly.

T.I. walked into the operating room, where everybody concerned had been apprised of the circumstances. The son of the world's richest man, as it was reputed, was about to have emergency neurosurgical decompression by Dr. Hoen, who normally never operates here, but now has been given very special permission. Dr. Hoen was to be given absolutely everything he wishes, and all courtesies, if you please!

Tom Hoen reopened J. Lawrence Poole's old incision and turned the bone flap in less than five minutes. T.I. Hoen was one hell of a surgeon when time is of the essence, and especially when he performed with an audience. He was always slick, smooth, and speedy—"poetry in motion," as some might say and when things were really important he looked, to even the most seasoned surgeon, like a magician. He achieved the absolute maximum out of every movement of his fingers and hands with the least amount of wasted effort.

Despite his awesome display of talent, T.I. could not safely attempt to remove the last bit of tumor, attached as it was to a vital brain structure, the hypothalamus. It was enough that his life was reprieved by the reduction of pressure at the base of his brain.

Following the surgery, when Timothy had stabilized sufficiently, Theodora, after T.I. agreed that he could be transferred to University Hospital at this point, again waved off any attempts by the hospital authorities to keep her son at Columbia-Presbyterian. One would think that there was a battle going on between Columbia and NYU, as to who could "capture" Timothy. I suppose that is exactly what it amounted to. Competition between topnotch institutions can be severe.

One thing was absolutely certain—Theodora Getty was in

the driver's seat and called all the shots. Theodora paid exceptionally close attention to Timothy's problem. Not much escaped her. She knew, for example, that Timothy almost died a second time at NYU, because of "adrenal crisis." This was associated with diabetes insipidus, an outpouring of the body's water resources. Timothy was rescued by a team of internists and endocrinologists, especially by a senior neurosurgical resident from Nicaragua, my predecessor, named Hamilcar Rojas. Dr. Rojas was the first to recognize the dehydration from diabetes insipidus, causing false high sodium levels.

Dr. Rojas took complete charge, countermanding the orders of the chief of endocrinology and, as it turned out, saving Timothy's life again.

I mention the above because at this point I became "Johnny-on-the-spot," as the neurosurgical resident in immediate charge of Timothy's care. Moreover, I was designated to carry out a series of injections of an antitumor drug over a five-week period.

These consisted of alternating spinal taps and injections directly into his skull cavity, to bathe Timothy's remaining tumor tissue with methotrexate, an anti-tumor drug that killed his tumor cells that grew in Jane Wright's tissue cultures. Dr. Wright, a research oncologist, could test her growing tumor cells with an assortment of antitumor drugs much like an ordinary bacteriology lab tests antibiotics.

Theodora had spoken in the imperative. I lowered myself into the chair she indicated, and we talked. I already had given Timothy two of his novel chemotherapy treatments, by first injecting a tiny bit of local anesthetic into the skin, either in the lower spine or in the right side of the scalp after shaving a small area, depending on which area was to receive the methotrexate. Theodora would sit calmly, holding Timothy's hand as I performed the procedure, watching silently. Timothy would wince ever so slightly, as I gave him the novocaine. Theodora was very pleased with my technical skills, my attitude, my compassion for Timothy, and just about everything else. What could she possibly want to discuss?

I found out immediately. "I think, Dr. Bloom, that we can alter your injection technique and, mind you, you are truly skillful at it, but I would like to eliminate all pain for Timothy."

"Teddie," as she insisted I call her. "Exactly what do you have in mind? The preliminary novocaine causes a tiny twinge, I must admit."

"I know my son well, Dr. Bloom. We are Christian Scientists. Let's try it my way. Let me read to Timothy from the Scriptures. He will gradually become more and more relaxed.

"When I know he is in just the right state, I will nod to you when he is ready."

When Teddie stares at someone straight in the eye, it is difficult to ignore her wishes. I, for one, was not only willing to comply; it occurred to me that it just might work.

Let Teddie think it was religion. I would silently regard it as a form of hypnosis!

Teddie lifted the massive, antique-looking bible from her bedside table and accompanied me through the connecting door to Timothy's room. As we walked, I wondered how much her religion contributed to her supreme self-assurance and perpetual poise. I know she prayed often.

"Hi, Timoshenko," I greeted the pale lad with the blank look on his face. T.I. always used this name, alluding to a general in the Russian Army. This always got a rousing smile out of the boy.

"How are you, Dr. Bloom," he replied, his face lighting up. 'You want me on my side?" His eyes followed me to his bedside. Though now legally blind, Timothy still could make out light and dark and detect crude shapes.

I removed the methotrexate from my pocket and opened the spinal tray. Teddie had begun to read from her text. She was now mother, nurse, and religious practitioner simultaneously. We would learn very shortly if her prediction would materialize.

After reading for two or three minutes Theodora gave me the awaited nod. I quietly injected the local with no reaction from Timothy. In went the spinal needle to the right place, out came the spinal fluid. In went the methotrexate and out came the spinal needle with a quick pull. Not a single sign of pain! It was just the result that Teddie had predicted, and the one we had both hoped for. I concealed my amazement.

In every future injection, Timothy was never to flinch. There was never the slightest flicker of a painful response. Was it a form of "local" or "general" anesthesia? I never could work out the physiologic mechanisms. Timothy was never quite asleep. He seemed to enter a trance-like state, and yet some would say it was faith. What difference does it make what you call it, as long as it works?

Teddie invited me to join her for cocktails at the Pierre Hotel one late afternoon. It was exciting to be out on the town with one very sophisticated lady in a hotel owned by her husband. I was curious about her past experiences as a war correspondent and as trustee of various New York City museums and other institutions. At about the second drink, she got somewhat more to the point. Catching me in eye contact, she said, "You have been just terrific with my Timothy, and I believe you deserve some kind of reward. Just tell me what you want?"

Oh my, but she was straightforward, direct, and sudden with her approach! I was definitely flustered, embarrassed, and probably even blushing. I really did not know what to say. Teddie silently awaited my belated reply. Finally, I murmured, "I'm just doing my job, I'm glad you're grateful, I really don't need anything."

The following day, Theodora handed me two tickets for *My Fair Lady*, then playing on Broadway. I must say I enjoyed bringing my sister, Shirley, there on the back of my little motor scooter. We sat in the middle of the first row. Theodora was determined to show her appreciation and that was good enough for me.

The next time I was in her room, I remember meeting Clyde Beatty, the famous circus performer and lion tamer. Teddie remarked to him, "Dr. Bloom rides around the streets of New York City on a little motor scooter." Beatty remarked, "Let me congratulate you for your courage," and shook my hand. I left the room beaming with this special recognition by a man of supreme bravery.

One late development was Timothy's cranial contour. T.I. noted that there was a bit of a deformity developing in the operative site. We discussed it and wondered if it was increased pressure? T.I. thought we ought to re-operate to correct the deformity. We decided to give it a little more time to determine whether it would progress further.

That very weekend, T.I. flew to Paris, France to call upon Timothy's father and try to persuade him to donate to the New York University Medical School. While we were scrubbing up for a disc operation T.I. described his conversation with the oil tycoon.

The Paris hotel room that Getty lived in was not at all lavish, and T.I. was surprised by this. He thought asking for a million dollars was a very reasonable request of a billionaire. His son's life had been saved and all medical and surgical fees would have been waived. The response was crass, T.I. thought.

"I am in the business of making money," Getty had replied, "not giving it away. Just send your bill to my attorneys when you're finished. There will be no donations." Getty had made himself eminently clear and T.I. had no reason to talk to him any longer. The 6,000 mile trip had been a total waste!

Timothy's operation was carried out on a Thursday morning. It was supposed to be a relatively minor operation, although it was, of course, done under general anesthesia, which automatically classifies it as a major procedure.

The surgery went well, and it looked like we were just about ready to close, when T.I. leaned over and in a semi-whisper said, "While we're in Timothy's head, I don't suppose it would harm him if we took a look underneath the frontal lobe to see what's happened to the tumor?" I nodded in assent with a slight twinge of reluctance but not enough to make an issue out of it. We extended the incision a bit to where we could get a look under the frontal lobe.

We observed no visible tumor, none at all. There was a trace of jubilation in T.I.'s manner, which I must say, was very well restrained.

We had achieved our objective, it seemed. We were even more jubilant when, after waiting for him to come out of anesthesia, Timothy seemed his old self, just as he was preoperatively.

I set about the following afternoon on a weekend away, in a good state of mind.

How pleased Theodora must be. I was not prepared for the shock that I would receive early Monday morning.

I sensed the bad news on the face of my junior resident as soon as I arrived.

"The Getty boy is dead," he declared in a solemn tone. Several seconds of silence elapsed as the gravity of his words flooded my mind. I lowered myself into a chair.

"What happened?" I asked. "He looked good immediately post-op."

"Another adrenal crisis, just like after the previous procedure, dehydration, diabetes insipidus. All hell broke loose. He went fast. Carlos called everybody, but no use, it was straight downhill."

T.I. was due any moment for rounds on his private patients. He appeared very somber when he finally approached, and I awaited his opening remarks.

"Why did you go away this weekend, Bill?" I could see what was coming, and I decided to hold firm.

"Because it was my weekend off," I said. "Carlos was covering."

In his unflinching manner, T.I. said simply, "Carlos is not

Bill Bloom, and this was Timothy Getty." He awaited my response. Tom Hoen was of the old school that says you sit on your residents hard and the more they suffer the better it is for them.

I finally spoke. 'You make me feel good and bad at the same time. All you had to do was tell me to stay, I could have canceled my plans. Not that it would have necessarily made a difference," I added. I just had to hold my ground and avoid the guilt trip he was throwing at me.

T.I. could not rebut me at this point. After all, he had the entire team available to him to watch for postoperative complications, and it was a good team. The remorse he tried to instill in me did not work. It was not an unfriendly encounter. We knew each other quite well by that time, and I knew he was proud of me as a trainee. It was T.I.'s wife who told me, never T.I. himself.

T.I. then related that he had just talked to Theodora and the head of the Christian Science Church in Boston and special permission was arranged for an autopsy. He hoped that I would write a case report about Timothy for publication, insofar as we had used unusual and special techniques for instilling a chemotherapeutic agent and regardless of the findings on postmortem, it would be of great interest to the medical profession and the neurosurgical fraternity, in particular. T.I.'s wishes would be fulfilled, I assured him.

The time for the final goodbye to Theodora arrived. I wondered how she would react, how I might say a reassuring word. I met her in the "Getty suite," now with an empty room. She greeted me in a graceful and solemn fashion, with only the barest touch of formality. Her eyes were dry, her make-up unsullied.

"T.I. and you and all the others did your very best. It simply wasn't meant to be." I wanted to say something reassuring, but soon realized that it was Theodora doing all of the reassuring. The tears were in my eyes alone.

I was about to wish her well in her future life when she became more confidential than she had ever been. Her relationship with John Paul Getty was over. There was another man whom she loved. Tragic though the death of Timothy had been, she would be starting a new life. In fact, she already had planned well into the future.

Theodora, if you are still alive and well after these 40 years, it is my turn to take you to the Pierre Hotel for cocktails. We will toast the memory of Timothy, that brave son of yours, who, if he had made it to manhood, would have been a perfect world-class gentleman. For the second drink, we will toast you, Theodora, and what you taught me about the enormous powers of faith, an unforgettable experience. And, if we have a third drink, we shall toast both your God and mine. After all, she could very well be one and the same.

Chapter 8

We Are The Best, Aren't We?

As chief resident in neurosurgery on the NYU service at Bellevue Hospital in 1959, I befriended a colleague of unusual talent. This diminutive woman, Elizabeth Coryllos, was chief surgical resident and was slated to become America's first female pediatric surgeon. Our paths crossed very often in the emergency room, in the operating room, in the cafeteria, and occasionally, in each other's room. Betty, as she preferred to be called, had become a very dear friend and soulmate, a relationship akin to brother and sister, with considerable mutual admiration thrown in.

Betty was seasoned and polished. Her father, a great patriot, emigrated to America from Greece, distinguishing himself here as a chest surgeon. He also brought over his own dear friend Dr. Papanicolaou, who became famous for the "Pap smear," a test that since has saved hundreds of thousands of women's lives.

At supper in the cafeteria, one Thursday evening, Betty reminded me that our long-awaited unique shunt operation on a baby with a large head was about to take place the following morning.

"I'm ready," I said. "Will our supervisors be present? After all, this operation has never been done before."

Betty grinned. "No, sweet William, just the two of us. Why do we need them? We are the best, aren't we?" My question was answered. I had faith in myself, but it was always enhanced by our special bond of fellowship. We were both completing the most critical, exciting periods in our respective careers, but it was also the most demanding, exhaustive, and stressful.

The surgical department and the neurosurgical department figured that excess fluid from the brain cavity could be best drained off into the body's only tissue that really was created to absorb fluid, namely the intestinal wall. Two weeks earlier, Betty had opened the baby's belly, tied off five or six inches of small intestine, re-anastomosed the intestine, and converted the isolated loop into a blind sac. Then the baby was given a recently-discovered sulfa drug that killed off all the bacteria within the bowel. Now, without worrying about infections, a catheter could be placed in the brain cavity and tunneled under the skin to the abdomen where we would insert the other end of it into the isolated bowel loop and ... voila! The water on the brain would drain off perpetually without a pressure build up, leaving a normal-sized brain cavity—they hoped!

Operations for hydrocephalus had been invented and reinvented for decades, but this had a certain promise and rationale that stirred me.

The next morning, in the operating room, I was enthusiastic and secure, knowing I had a supremely cool young woman to assist me in the first part of the operation. I had seven assistant residents I could have called upon to help and Betty had fourteen assistant residents in her department. We needed none of them since we could assist each other, and we preferred it that way.

The female baby with the enlarged head was under anesthesia, lying on her left side. I made a small skin opening above and behind the tiny patient's right ear and inserted a little instrument to hold the scalp edges apart while I drilled a small hole in the skull about 1/3 of an inch in diameter. I cauterized the surface of the brain and its lining and passed a thin metal tube cautiously, slowly into the brain cavity. Fluid squirted out under pressure. After two minutes with the metal tube in, I removed it and passed one end of the sterile rubber urinary catheter into the brain cavity. It was just long enough to reach the belly in this three-month-old baby, though it was designed for passing up into the bladder of adults.

Betty made a little opening in the neck and I tunneled the catheter under the skin down to her. She then made a little opening in the skin over the chest, and I passed the catheter down to that opening. She then made the third opening over the right side of the belly, a full size incision, and we tunneled the catheter to that point.

Now, the catheter extended from within the brain cavity out of the skull but under the skin, down the neck and chest to the belly incision. It remained for Betty to place the other end into the specially prepared bowel sac under the belly wall. She took over for the rest of the operation. Now I was assisting her. So far, we had lost less than a teaspoonful of blood. We had been very cautious, knowing blood loss can be a big problem in small babies.

As usual, Betty worked deftly and neatly, better than many attending surgeons that I have worked with. Here we were, down in the baby's belly cavity. Betty proudly showed me the healthy looking isolated loop of the ileum, its blood supply intact. It didn't move, unlike the rest of the bowel. She made a little slit in it, and we placed the catheter tip within it. Betty closed it with a purse-string suture that held it snugly in place. Then we closed all four incisions.

"Hey, we're not bad as plumbers," I remarked, getting a little smile out of her that even her mask couldn't hide!

A few minutes later, after finishing writing on the chart, we looked at each other blankly. Little was spoken. We had tons of work awaiting us. We agreed to meet in Betty's room at about 10 p.m. We each kept a key to the other's room.

After the weekly neurosurgical departmental conference, several emergency consultations, performing an operation for a bullet wound to the brain, and helping a junior resident reduce a dislocated neck, I finally entered Betty's room. It must have been midnight. The room was empty. The bed had not been slept in.

I called the pediatric nurse and learned our baby was drinking sugared water from a bottle via a nipple. So far so good, for our historic first, but I needed some reassurance from Betty and her remarkable good judgment. Her very presence was a kind of medicine for me, and I think I was something like that for her. We supported each other in terms of morale, something like close buddies on a battlefront during war.

At 1 a.m., Betty entered and very nearly stumbled over my corpse-like body. I had dozed off on the floor, with a slight backache, for a blissful, restful 45 minutes waiting for her. I saw that Betty was also dangerously exhausted, even a trifle pale. I worried about her. We each admitted to the other that we had been up all night the night before except for perhaps two or three merciful hours of rest.

Betty literally flopped into bed, remaining motionless, still wearing her green operative scrubs, knowing she could be called again any minute or any hour during the night. "You're welcome onto the bed, Billy boy," she kidded. "That's onto as opposed to into, you realize."

I tried to laugh, but I was too tired. I was quite comfortable on the floor. Sleepily, I remarked, "Betty, think of it. We did the world's first ventriculo-ileoentectomy shunt."

"So what," she retorted, "it's no honor unless it works."

"It's going to work," I insisted. "Now that we have the means to sterilize the bowel, our procedure will be the best ever devised. It's going to work, I just know it." I was drifting off, but I had just enough energy for one more comment.

"Betty," I said, "If you don't solve your love problems, I just want you to know that you can always marry me. I'll have you." This was my way of testing to determine whether her brain was still half-way alert.

"William, my dear," she replied, "you are indeed my favorite soulmate, but—" and I heard her snoring a trifle.

The baby's body grew while the head shrunk a little over the next two months. The head was normal for the body size by then. Five years later, I learned from Betty, the body was still doing "beautifully" with her ventriculo-ileoentectomy. Since the Holter one-way valve came out during this time, we saw no point in publishing our success. The new one-way valves were superior to our simple urinary catheter and required but a single operation. The very expression ventriculo-ileoentectomy is unknown. The phrase does not appear in any textbook, not in any journal. It means absolutely nothing to anyone except for Betty and myself. Well, possibly one other person. She should be about forty years old as I write these words.

Chapter 9

Wielders Of Axes And Knives

Traumatology - the study of trauma - has to be interwoven with the name of Bellevue Hospital, a legendary place synonymous with injuries and emergencies.

I recall the night when, as chief resident in neurosurgery, I was called to the emergency room to examine Arturo Gomera, a victim of an axe wound to the head.

Arturo wasn't in too bad shape. He was only slightly drowsy and had perfect orientation. I deduced that his brain was not particularly injured despite the appalling condition of his scalp. Surely, there must be a story behind this. I asked Arturo for the details.

A group of Hispanics living in a residential hotel had teamed up into couples. Arturo's girlfriend was next door having drinks with that particular couple, and when he put his ear to the door, he heard his girlfriend say to the couple, "What? To have Arturo, ha! I would rather have a woman than to have Arturo."

Arturo was a macho man and happened to have a small axe in the closet of his room. After fetching his axe he first chopped down the entrance door and leaped through the new opening he created. The startled occupants were not exactly ready to welcome him. With his axe he now faced three frightened souls, his girlfriend and the wicked couple. Whatever words were exchanged, Arturo, axe in hand, assaulted all three of them, starting with his girlfriend. With a chopping motion to her head he felled her and then went for the other woman. He chopped at her scalp until she also fell to the floor. He then had to contend with a tough male who gave him a struggle. Though he may have lacerated the scalp of his opponent, it didn't injure the man's brain. At least he was able to wrest away the axe from Arturo and chop at least three huge gashes in Arturo's scalp. All four protagonists were on the floor when ambulances carted Arturo off to Bellevue and the other three to another hospital on the West Side of Manhattan. Somebody on the scene wisely decided that it was best that Arturo be kept at some distance from the other three.

When I examined Arturo's head injuries I was eerily reminded of the bark of a tree and how, when a hatchet comes in at an angle, the bark curls up. Arturo's skull bone curled up in a similar fashion. I took him into the operating room and cleaned the wounds and clipped off the peculiar skull "shavings," something I have never seen again in my career.

From a human-interest standpoint, I have no follow up on Arturo and his acquaintances. I certainly have no reason to disbelieve his story.

Another fellow that I saw in the neurosurgical clinic, walking around, talking, obviously alive and well, told me a most incredible story of his own injury. A year earlier, he was assaulted by a burglar at the entrance of his apartment. The intruder wielded a long knife and thrusted it into our hero's head. The victim was so enraged at the burglar, that he looked down and picked up the knife. Broken, it was, but there was still four inches of blade attached to the handle on the concrete entranceway. Reaching down and quickly grabbing the remains of the knife he plunged the blade into the abdomen of his assailant. The assailant went down. Our man then felt about two inches of knife blade in his left temple with considerable blood streaming down his left cheek and neck. He decided to run for the hospital, about a block away, to seek help.

What our friend didn't realize, as he ran for the hospital, was that the broken knifeblade had penetrated the left side of his scalp, right through his brain, and had come out the other side! It was only after he entered the hospital emergency room from his quick sprint that he realized there was blood also dripping from the right side of his scalp! By this time, he noticed that his legs were getting quite weak. He had made it into the hospital emergency room just in time and yelled for some help.

The nurses must have seen an odd sight- blood streaming down both sides of the man's head with a blade sticking out on either side. Neurosurgeons were called. By the time they arrived he had lost the use of both arms and both legs. He was still able to talk, but only for a short time, as he quickly went into a semi-comatose and then a comatose state. He was rushed to the operating room where he spent several hours while neurosurgeons gingerly extricated the weapon from his head. Apparently, all of the major blood vessels of the brain were missed, miraculously. The lucky man gradually recovered over a period of three to four months being able to leave the rehabilitation department and limp around shortly thereafter. He had also regained good use of his arms.

From the chain of events I would deduce this was brain swelling that was largely responsible for the developing weakness of all four limbs. How this man actually survived and how he was able to sprint to the hospital is miraculous, even to me.

Oh yes, what happened to the other guy? The assailant and would-be murderer, with four inches of knife in his belly, had almost as bad a time of it, I believe.

On my last day as chief resident at Bellevue, I had to confront another great challenge, one involving the spinal cord instead of the brain. In this instance, the knife went straight through a man's upper dorsal spine, vertically through the spinal cord, continuing into and through the body of the vertebra and ending up in the chest cavity. Here, we were faced with a most interesting situation and a great challenge for me personally. I called in the chest surgeons, who felt that they should first explore the chest for possible injury to major blood vessels and to the lung, itself. I watched the chest surgeons complete their exploration and then took over the case.

We turned the man onto his belly, still under general anesthesia. My big problem here was getting the knife out without injuring the spinal cord, which it had penetrated exactly in the midline in a vertical plane. It hadn't really damaged the spinal cord too badly. The man moved his legs nicely. Had the knife gone in horizontally instead of vertically, he would have been totally and permanently paralyzed with all sensation lost below that level.

I did my usual approach to the spinal cord. The knife blade was, miraculously, in the exact center of the spinal cord and I realized there was about another three and a half or four inches of blade that I could not see. I had both hands on the handle and pulled slowly and gradually. Nothing happened. You can imagine if a knife were sticking into a tree far enough, you would not be able to pull it out without enormous strength. This is about what I was facing here.

I may have had the strength to actually pull it out, but in doing so, I might suddenly lurch and damage this young man's spinal cord. Always with both hands on the knife handle, I finally manipulated it up and down, perhaps one or two millimeters at a time. About 40 or 50 such movements took place when I realized the knife could be extracted slowly, gently, carefully, both hands on the knife handle, cautious not to cause lateral pressure at any time against the cord. There is an operation called a myelotomy, a special operation for pain relief where one deliberately incises the cord in similar fashion.

I kept pulling gently but firmly with the little up and down movements, withdrawing the blade from the lung, the vertebral body, the spinal cord, the dura, and finally completely out of the patient. I placed the knife on the tray and said jocularly to the nurse, "Specimen," I said, awaiting her smile. We both knew it had to go to the police, not the laboratory.

I hope the patient recovered nicely, but I simply do not know. The next day I said goodbye to Bellevue Hospital and left for London, England.

Chapter 10

Queen Square and Wimbledon

Wylie McKissock, later to become Sir Wylie, accepted me as one of his research assistants for six months at St. George's Hospital and at National Hospital for Nervous Diseases, Queen Square, renowned as a world center for neurology for a century. McKissock admired my curiosity and productivity and, after six months, gave me a raise of 25 pounds per month and asked if I would stay an additional six months. During the year we produced seven publications including some classics on subdural hematomas and epidural hematomas, (collections of blood between the bone and the brain after injury), the largest series in the English language at the time.

McKissock was most noted for his work on subarachnoid hemorrhage and intracranial aneurysms. His expertise in surgery allowed sixty percent of all subarachnoid hemorrhages in southern England to be admitted under his care. One of my jobs was to photograph each blood vessel study (angiogram). In that year, I studied over 350 aneurysms, more than many neurosurgeons see in their entire careers.

McKissock enjoyed amazing his many visitors, and neurosurgeons came from around the world to meet him or see him operate. One source of amazement was the primitiveness of his St. George's operating room. You'd think Britain was a third world nation. The National Health Service hadn't spent a penny here, visitors would conclude. Doctors and nurses changed their clothes in a single change room, one gender at a time, to be sure. There was only one sink to scrub in and the intravenous sets were the same as those used in World War II! Foreigners were aghast and disbelieving, asking "Sir, how can you work under these conditions?" McKissock would smile instead of answering, deriving a kind of impish pleasure from their incredulity.

One day in Wimbledon was set aside for wining and dining together, an annual event about which I was duly warned by my colleagues. The boss took twelve of us to the best local restaurant for a seven-course lunch, with a different wine for each course. Wylie McKissock was a hard-working and hard-drinking Scotsman who would follow this food and wine orgy with a party at his own home, lasting several more hours. This eventually put a great strain on those who had a low tolerance for alcohol, since nobody wanted to offend the Chief by refusing the drinks offered.

Two of the boys passed out and had to be chauffeured back to their rooms in the resident quarters. This was average according to the trainees who attended the event in previous years.

The following day McKissock, as soon as he set eyes on me, inquired "Well, Bloom, what do you think of British drinking?"

"Awesome, sir, simply awesome," I answered with a straight face, thinking how lucky I was to maintain full consciousness the entire previous day.

McKissock was bluff and hearty on the surface, but also kindly and attentive to those who worked with him, whenever special attention was necessary. Sort of a father figure or a mother hen looking after the "little ones." He invented a little game whereby we would present color slides to each other and each person present would assign a number based on the quality of the others' film, the one with the most points was declared the winner. McKissock would win about thirty percent of the time, probably due to his experience with a camera, and possibly abetted by his "chickens" who tended to fawn over the mother hen.

The day I first met McKissock was in his Queens Square office. He chatted with me a few minutes then looked at his watch, "Forgive me, Bloom, but I'm due in the O.R. You're welcome to watch, it's a posterior fossa meningioma. Should take me about 45 minutes." He obviously prided himself for his precision and accuracy, as well as speed.

He operated and I observed. He finished the procedure in the time allotted by himself and casually resumed our "interview." We hadn't met previously. He had accepted me on the strength of Tom Hoen's recommendation. I congratulated him on his skill and sense of organization. His O.R. nurse had been with him for twelve years. Conversation was minimal during the surgery. It had proceeded like a well-engineered and well-oiled machine. The rumor that McKissock was one of the slickest ever in the operating room was well-founded.

I was pleased when McKissock stuck a pin in New York on the globe he kept in his office. The geographical location of his trainees and research assistants around the world gave him a sense of importance as a teacher. Even though I had already been fully trained prior to my London experience, he liked me as a colleague that almost matched him for energy and love of achievement if not in organizational skills.

"I suspect that at Bellevue we weren't doing the right thing for subdural hematomas," I told him. "Four patients at death's door had only burr holes under local , with a drain, being too sick for general anesthesia."

"Here, Bloom, we do all of them with burr holes, with rare exception," he told me. "There's no need to remove the membranes."

"I agree sir, but our policy was to do major surgery. In those four cases I went back a day later and did the craniotomy and in every case the brain had reexpanded. That convinced me that minor surgery is better than major. Even Walter Dandy did the craniotomy routinely and had a high incidence of post-op epidurals."

McKissock agreed. Just by chance one of his research fellows, Alan Richardson, was working on a clinical research project, and found 389 cases of subdural hematoma. It would be the largest scientific study ever undertaken on this complication of head injury. McKissock invited me to join them in the study. Alan and I put many hundreds of hours, each of us, on the massive project. We made primary data charts, secondary data charts and tertiary data charts. We spent six or seven months gathering data, interpreting it and drawing our conclusions. We wanted it to be not only the biggest but the best study ever carried out. We eventually published it in *The Lancet*. Only two series of 300 cases or more had been published earlier, one from Bellevue Hospital and another from Kings County Hospital in Brooklyn.

One of the Americans, B. Cone Pevehouse, suggested that we use the same material to study the eye findings in this condition. Cone did most of the work on this paper. Eventually we published in the American journal simply called "Neurology" (often called the "green journal" based on the color of the cover).

Then Julien Taylor, another of McKissock's research assistants, worked with us on the subject of epidural hematomas. These are generally arterial bleeders outside the dura, but also between the brain and skull bone. They often go faster and have to be recognized more quickly and early. Timely recognition and intervention is absolutely vital, inasmuch as the big bleeds invariably lead to death, often within a very few hours. This is considered neurosurgery's most emergent complication of head injury. Formerly, the "lucid interval" was the key to diagnosis but we discovered, in our 125 cases, that a lucid interval occurred only in twenty-eight percent of the surgical cases of epidural ("extradural," as they are called in England) hematoma.

It became clear that the initial unconsciousness, when it occurred was a "concussion," a direct effect on the brain from the blow to the head. After the lucid interval, if it occurred, a secondary problem developed, namely, the bleeding and its attendant compression of the brain. Blows to the head would fracture the thin temporal bone, the sharp edge of which would nick the little "meningeal" artery lying in a groove in the inner surface of the skull. Each pulse would bring a drop or two out of the vessel and within an hour or perhaps two or three the "clot" would reach a sizable volume. The pupil would enlarge on the same side. The pulse would slow. The opposite limbs would weaken, and the patient would go on to decerebration and death.

This paper, also in *The Lancet*, remained much quoted for the next two or three decades. It certainly helped develop my own "feeling" or "instinct" as how to manage head injuries.

Another of our six publications that year was an Atlas of Positive-Contrast Myelography. It had to do with understanding what goes on in the spinal canal. Invented over thirty years earlier, it antedated CT scans by four decades and was invaluable in diagnosing herniated discs and other causes of trouble relating to pressure on the spinal cord or the nerve roots that come off it. It still is valuable at times but CT and MRI scans have replaced most myelograms.

In the spring of 1960, I entered the office of a doctor at the Royal Marsden Hospital with some photographs, color slides and a "now-do-you-believe-me" attitude.

Five months earlier I told him that I could grow malignant brain tumor outside the brain in patients, and in fact was part of a team in New York that had already done it. The doctor, considered the dean of British oncology (study of tumors), simply refused to believe me. "Come back," he said, "when you have photos or slides to prove it."

Since brain tumors kill by exerting pressure on the surrounding normal brain and never spontaneously metastasized (spread through the blood stream to other tissues) it was generally assumed that transplanted brain tumors could not possibly "take."

McKissock supported my special project, to inoculate the brain tumor into subcutaneous tissues where they could interact with the lymph system and perhaps build up antibodies. The central nervous system is the only organ system in the body that does not have access to the lymphatic system. We were trying to harness the body's own mechanisms to reduce the growth potential of malignant gliomas, a real killer.

The noted neuropathologist Harry Zimmerman had suggested that gliomas might be inhibited by immune mechanisms, having spent years expanding the knowledge of the biology of these tumors. By implanting crystals of a mothball-like substance in a rat's brain he actually created gliomas and then transplanted them to other animals.

As I predicted the British scientist was totally honest, apologetic to the extreme and treated me with enormous new found respect.

"Come show your material to my research staff," he said. "we're just about ready for our usual meeting."

At the conference, I told the assembled group my hopes for the future treatment of malignant gliomas, since surgery, radiation and chemotherapy were so limited, we must explore the immunological possibilities.

The prestigious British medical journal, *The Lancet,* published the results of my project a couple of months later. The British and Americans soon, with some enthusiasm, developed the new science of neuro-immunology. One North Carolina neurosurgeon actually spent his entire research career in neuro-immunology. It is quite possible, I believe, that a significant breakthrough in neuro-immunology could very well render all previous treatments of glioma obsolete.

Malignant glioma, often termed "brain cancer," remains a great challenge. Between killing George Gershwin in the 1930s and Cardinal John O'Connor recently and many thousands in between, it has posed a serious and almost overwhelming problem for patients and families as well as for those of us who have taken care of them. As with other problems in medicine, we hope the human race will come up with heroes of science to mitigate the ills that beset us. A breakthrough is always just around the corner, it seems.

Not long after I left McKissock other Americans served in his department, including John Jayne, who went on to become Chairman of Neurosurgery at the University of Virginia, editor of the prestigious *Journal of Neurosurgery*, and mentor of the greatest actual number of department heads in American institutions since the great Harvey Cushing.

McKissock had received an O.B.E., Order of the British Empire, before I met him and eventually was knighted by Queen Elizabeth for his contributions to the science of neurological surgery. He said he would retire the day he was to be knighted. No one believed him.

According to John Potter, a British neurosurgeon who became director of postgraduate education at Oxford, Wylie McKissock did exactly what he said he would do. He retired, moved back to his native Scotland, enjoyed life as a raconteur, undoubtedly still pouring drinks for his listeners until the end of his days.

Chapter 11

Sir Geoffrey Jefferson

"Don't worry, Sir Geoff is a regular guy," T. I. Hoen assured me on my last visit to his home prior to my departure for London. I would be working in London but with Wiley McKissock. T. I. wanted me to look up his dear friend, Sir Geoffrey Jefferson, and I had inquired about how one addresses a knight.

From London I wrote to Sir Geoffrey, and he invited me to stop by when it was convenient, merely to call first. I had done just that, so, while en route to Scotland in my Austin Healy Sprite, I stopped in for tea.

Arriving at Sir Geoffrey's home in a suburban part of Manchester, I parked in the driveway and awaited his arrival. When he finally pulled in, he walked to the opposite side to help Lady Jefferson out of the car. I overheard him whisper, "You remember Tom Hoen, this is his resident, who is visiting."

Lady Jefferson had a blank expression on her face as she nodded. A certain delayed impact took place when I realized how incapable she was of speech or almost any form of communication.

I was indeed in the presence of a great man, a man obviously capable of great love. Lady Jefferson previously had been a psychiatrist and, originally, one of his own students. Of their three children, one was a neurologist and another a neurosurgeon.

While a servant took over and cared for Lady Jefferson, Sir Geoffrey ushered me into his library. There were, literally, thousands of books. He pulled a book out of one of his shelves, turned the cover, and one could easily make out the handwriting of the owner, but it looked like that of a school boy who had written his name in to identify the book as his own. The name was clear—it was the signature of Isaac Newton! This had been one of his books at Cambridge University some 300 years earlier.

He pulled out another book that Harvey Cushing had given him many years ago and was inscribed by Cushing in Latin, one of the words misspelled.

"Look," Sir Geoffrey beamed, as he recalled Cushing presenting him the book. "The bastard wouldn't admit that he had a problem spelling the word." Jefferson laughed again.

We had nothing but the greatest respect for Harvey Cushing as a man and as the virtual founder of our specialty. Jefferson had spent time with Cushing in Boston back in the 20s. He was referring to one of Cushing's idiosyncrasies, an inability to admit he could be wrong.

As tea was served, I mentioned that I was interested in doing some scientific writing while in England.

"But Bloom," Jefferson paused, "can you write?" He was looking me straight in the eye, and I was fumbling for my answer when he responded with a sorry look on his face, "Oh-oh-oh, that was such a brutal question." Sir Geoff was crisp, incisive, and super-alert, but his humane qualities were never lacking.

Most of Jefferson's associates and trainees rather looked down upon St. George's as a surgical factory and not primarily as an academic center. Some of this pride was false, however, since St. George's was coming up fast, and Wylie McKissock would receive his knighthood someday. Jamie Ambrose, a neuroradiologist who worked with us, would introduce to the medical world CT scans (originally EMI scans) at St. George's, recognizing the potential of Geoffrey Hounsfield's brilliant invention, forever changing the way all clinical neuroscience is practiced.

All at once, an exceedingly charming and gracious young woman burst in upon us with scarcely a knock on the door. She was obviously very much at home, and Sir Geoffrey explained why. Her late father, "a truly great writer and editor," was Geoffrey Jefferson's boyhood pal.

They grew up in the same home town together. Each of them rose to the top of their respective fields, Wadsworth, as the great liberal editor of the *Manchester Guardian* and, of course, Sir Geoffrey, as the dean of British neurosurgeons.

Janet Wadsworth, an only child whose parents were recently deceased, had her parents' home in Derbyshire, and she was to invite me there to visit with friends, as well as to introduce me to her friends in London. It was at her place, in the little village of OverHaddon, where I proposed to my future wife. It was a village where the most recent home was built 150 years earlier and no homes were made of wood, all were sturdily constructed of stone.

As Janet and I chatted in Sir Geoffrey's driveway, she remarked, "Don't turn your head, but Sir Geoffrey is watching us from the second floor, he doesn't like to miss a trick." I was carrying a gift that Sir Geoffrey gave me to bring back to T. I. Hoen for his recently-married son. Years later, before her premature death from cancer, Janet visited us in Bay Shore, Long Island, where she met our older son, Jeffrey, named for Sir Geoffrey, her spiritual godfather.

Sir Geoffrey Jefferson was indeed a leader, a teacher, a writer, a scientist, an orator, a doctor, a surgeon and, in every one of these categories, a class act. Thomas Hoen's description of Sir Geoff as a "regular guy" meant only that Jefferson had no airs, no complexes.

Though I have met other intellectual giants, Jefferson was the most inspiring. He certainly left his mark on me, and without a doubt on anyone who had the opportunity to know him. Months later at a meeting of the British Neurosurgical Society in Edinburgh, he clearly stood out as doyen of the group, and in fact was its founder and permanent unofficial leader until his death a year or so later.

Chapter 12

In the Land of the Vikings

The Swedes, having been neutral in the recent World Wars, seemed to be an affluent people. Certainly they spent a lot on their hospital and healthcare system. When I proceeded from England to Lund, I found myself in a modern firstclass hospital with no more than two beds to a room, the latest equipment and the very best in x-ray and other technology. Of course, both countries had a similar socialized medicine system. It was joked that the Swedes built their hospitals starting with an x-ray department and a research unit.

I was now the recipient of a fellowship given to a non-Scandinavian. This implies the fellowship could not be awarded a Swede, Norwegian, Dane, Finn or Icelander. I would be working with Dr. Lars Leksell in his unit at the University of Lund. Leksell, himself was involved that summer in various projects and his associate, Stig Jeppsson, would be my immediate superior.

I had just finished our book, *Atlas of Positive Contrast Myelography*, and was shocked to know that the neuroradiologists at Lund didn't know about injecting oil-based "dyes" into the spine. They had either injected air, which was not as effective as the "dyes" or water-soluble dyes, which are rather painful.

Sweden was actually the birthplace of neuroradiology. Herbert Olivacrona, father of Swedish neurosurgery, had trained a radiologist by the name of Lysholm to specifically develop techniques for neurosurgical cases. Lysholm and Lindgren fathered the science of neuroradiology much as Cushing had fathered modern neurosurgery. James Bull, who co-authored our *Atlas of Myelography* became the father of neuroradiology in Great Britain and in the early 1960s neuroradiology developed rapidly in the United States as well.

Angiography was introduced by the Portuguese neurologist, Dr. Egaz Moniz, but it was in Sweden that the technology made the most rapid advances. A single injection in the carotid artery reveals the arteries, capillaries and veins within the brain.

Dr. Jeppsson had been a professor of physical chemistry prior to becoming a neurosurgeon and was involved in a project studying ultrasound of the brain. I was pleased to participate in this non-invasive procedure. We could get an idea of whether the brain was shifted by bouncing sound waves off the calcium deposits, particularly the pineal gland located centrally in the middle of the brain. When the pineal was shifted by a tumor or any other mass, this would be a tip-off to which side of the brain the mass was on. Eventually ultrasound would be refined for intraoperative use and it is now often used in the operating rooms of large centers in a way that virtually tells the surgeon which way to go to get to the tumor.

Barbara, my wife, had joined me in Sweden and we lived in an apartment provided us by Per Nilsson. Per had to be in the North of Sweden on an Air Force assignment and loaned me his apartment. His fiancee, Siv, was the chief nurse of the department of neurosurgery. Stig Jeppson and his wife threw a party for the department on August 15, the crawfish festival day throughout Sweden. It is a special day since the lakes of Sweden provide an abundance of crawfish that time of the year.

The Swedish sun does not set until about ten p.m. and the night is very short in August. What I didn't realize in advance was that this involves some serious drinking and there is not a lot of substance in the individual crawfish. They are simply very small.

After a few introductory drinks everyone gets quite tipsy and this is not reversed by the main course. It reminded me of Wylie McKissock's party. Perhaps Americans don't take drinking and partying quite as seriously as the Europeans. One or two people were on the verge of passing out, including my wife, Barbara. They were provided with beds while the rest of us piled into Stig's small boat. Everybody was feeling good, to put it mildly. I became fearful when we aimed the little boat toward Denmark. I sobered fast, assuming we were in deep water, way over our heads, as we putt-putted for about a mile. The others were all speaking Swedish, and when I interrupted to ask about water depth, someone replied "Only about eight feet!" My fear turned into a near panic.

Suddenly everybody whipped off their bathing suits as the boat stopped and dove into the water. I was last, I confess, because I was not used to these strange European habits, but eventually I got into the water realizing that the water was about four feet deep, and had never at any time been deeper. Someone had played a cruel joke on me.

There was only moonlight as a light source and at a certain point everybody got back in the boat and fifteen minutes later we were safely ashore, clad in our bathing suits and it was just about time to greet the rising sun.

This was scheduled to be an interesting day because Per Nilsson was coming back to take Barbara, Siv and myself up in a plane ride over the south of Sweden. That is precisely what happened. I was glad not to be the pilot, since I was suffering from severe fatigue and hoping that my blood alcohol level would diminish. In Sweden, it should be noted, one either spent the night with one's host or had a taxi arrive by pre-arrangement at a certain time to avoid arrest for drunken driving. One only needed the equivalent of two or three shots of whiskey to get to the blood level that would deprive you of your driver's license, carefully enforced in Sweden.

The summer of 1960 was exceedingly pleasant and we were

made to feel quite welcome. English was spoken by all physicians and most nurses, having replaced German as the second language of Sweden after WWII. Only the oldtimers that I saw as patients presented a language problem. It was indeed a pleasure to share ideas about surgery and science in a teaching center.

The University of Lund had been around for hundreds of years. The teaching system is interesting since one starts as a docent, or lecturer and then becomes an assistant and then an associate professor. When one makes that final jump to a full professor, the salary doubles along with the prestige. Full professorships in Sweden and in most European countries are not handed out as easily as in the United States. We joke about professors here, but in Europe it is important, quite a serious matter.

One of the doctors at the hospital was applying for a full professorship and had done his research on measuring pressures inside the cranium. He was given a tough time by the several professors of neurosurgery in Sweden, but finally got his reward. Ultimately, pressure monitors became sort of standard procedure in America and worldwide. Dr. Lundberg did science and neurosurgery a service by his seminal work on this subject. Likewise, a number if innovations by Professor Leksell have become standard. The Gamma knife, now currently used, is an outgrowth of Lars Leksell's original work.

Chapter 13

Rubenstein The Great

With wife and baby, and slightly into debt, I decided late in 1961 that it was time to get out in the world and make a living, and not rely on low-paying research grants.

I heard that Bob Rubenstein, a bit of a character, had a "hot practice" out on Long Island and was looking for an associate. Earlier, Dr. Tarlov, at New York Medical College, had offered me a post as an assistant professor at $5,000.00 a year, with additional compensation that could come from workers' compensation cases, something he wished to foist on any potential junior.

Even way back in the early 60s, when dollars bought so much more than they do today, I quickly realized that I would indeed have to live a lowly life for a time, at least.

Rubenstein seemed to take to me. He was an outgoing and dynamic individual, a mover and shaker who knew how to whip things into proper shape. He boasted how in two years he had tripled his practice and could scarcely keep up with the amount of surgery that needed to be done. He would pay me $1,000.00 a month and after a trial period on this salary, we could talk about a possible partnership. He spent a lot of time with me, ensuring that my arrangements for housing were good, and said that he would advance the money for a car for myself to get around to the various hospitals where he worked.

He was chief of two of the major hospitals in Eastern Nassau, including the increasingly prestigious East Nassau Community Hospital where his good friend, the chief of surgery, had made him chief of the Neurosurgical Department.

Later, I would learn that Bob would tend to abuse this power. He had made things increasingly tough for the neurosurgeons from other areas who came there to operate until, finally, at about the time I arrived on the scene, Bob, was doing all of the neurosurgery at the hospital by himself. He seemed to have an unlimited supply of energy, but I could easily understand why he was in almost desperate need of an assistant or associate.

I also admired his operative technique. No doubt about it, Bob was clever with his hands, and concentrated on making sure things went well in the operating room. This is, of course, something all surgeons do, but he had a certain charm that went along with his ability to lie, cheat, or stick it to his enemies.

Bob and I shared certain characteristics, but he had a lot of qualities that I lacked, particularly, a stage presence and a sense of dynamism. Later, I would realize that his unspoken credo was, "if you can't dazzle them with brilliance, baffle them with bull-doody." I personally wasn't so good at the bull-doody part, but had to admit that a little of that stuff could carry one a long way.

After I had been in practice with Bob for about two months, I realized, particularly after he had me deliver milk to his house when coming over for a conference, that I was being treated as a flunky and not an equal citizen. I made no protest, feeling that my chance to express myself would come in due course. I knew I was a far better clinician and diagnostician than Bob. On the other hand, he was more aggressive surgically, and would undertake advanced procedures that I might hesitate to carry out on my own.

On one occasion, I diagnosed the need for a hemispherectomy on a fifteen-year-old girl with a spastic left arm and leg. She had virtually uncontrollable epilepsy and was deteriorating. I had learned in Britain how, by removing most of one side of the brain, we could improve the patient's condition almost miraculously, and convinced Bob that this particular teenager needed the surgery. We mulled over that together, and he felt we could carry this out at East Nassau Hospital. This was a procedure that I had "discovered," and one that Bob Rubenstein, with his gifted hands, would carry out, assisted by yours truly.

Had the decision been unilaterally mine, I would have sent this patient to a major teaching center, with Bob taking the ultimate surgical responsibility since I had never performed this procedure myself or even assisted someone else. Now, I felt very good about what we were doing, and after it proved to be a smashing success, our hemispherectomy case made me realize that, although I was second fiddle in the operating room, there might be a future for the two of us together. Bob encouraged the idea wholeheartedly.

Six months had now gone by. Barbara, my wife, and baby Deborah were doing well. I now bought a car for Barbara so that she could get around on Long Island. My career was off and running, or so I thought.

A dilemma presented itself after we worked together for nearly a year. Bob wanted me to check two children he was admitting on a Sunday for cranioplasties on Monday. Both of the children had depressed fractures several months earlier and had "soft spots" where portions of their skull were missing. Bob intended to insert metal plates on both of them and had scheduled them for Monday morning.

He specifically asked me to write notes on the charts of these patients and, of course, the admitting orders had already been available in the admitting office, Bob having taken care of the arrangements both for admission and for the surgery.

On Sunday night, I felt the "soft spots." One was so small, I could scarcely detect an irregularity. This was a two-year-old child, who Bob had last seen two months earlier. At this age, the skull grows so fast that within another few weeks, there would be no palpable skull defect whatsoever.

I like to treat patients and their families as I would wish to be treated. I couldn't bring myself to write any notes on the charts of the two children since I didn't think that the surgery was necessary. The second child was a bit older. He had a somewhat larger opening. The big test would come the following day, one very critical to my future.

Early the following morning, I met a very irate and bombastic Dr. Rubenstein, who was at his unfriendliest.

"Meet me in my office at 4:30 this afternoon," he thundered. "I've got Van Buren helping me on the two cranioplasties. You've got the day off until 4:30."

I spent some time in thought that day. Barbara was now eight months pregnant with our second child. I had a feeling that Rubenstein was about to terminate our relationship. According to our contract, either one of us could terminate it at the end of any given month. One of the keys to my conclusion was his reference to "my office" instead of "our office." Up until this fateful weekend, it appeared that we would ultimately be partners.

"Don't worry, the money will flow like water, once you're established with me," Rubenstein had once told me. Was I stupid in not writing a short routine note on either chart simply because I felt it was ethically wrong to perform the surgery? It would have been so easy for me to have covered up my own feelings and write perfunctory notes on the hospital records which, of course, would indicate my approval of the surgery.

Rubenstein guessed rightly that I held back on the notes because of my honesty and his own blatant disregard for what was right, since he had the power, and from power stems the ability to control others.

How would Rubenstein dispose of me? Apparently, I had recently made vital decisions on my own, not in accordance with the position of "flunky." Rubenstein resented that. If we were ever to have been partners, it would have been on an unequal basis.

Rubenstein would be number one at all times. He would always have the power and control. It is customary to make a junior partner an equal partner at some time, within a year or two, but it could be as long as five years. Ultimately, the junior man wants to know he will be an equal partner.

The appointed time came, and Rubenstein faced me across his desk.

"You are fired. I am giving you a bonus of $1,500 so that you can find some part of the country where you are needed and wanted."

"But, Bob," I pointed out, "our contract says that it can be terminated only at the end of a month."

"If you're not out of my office in forty-eight hours, I'll have the police throw you out!" he said menacingly.

Rubenstein was indeed a little Napoleon. I wondered if he treated his wife as he treated me—his assistant, associate, colleague, and would-be future partner. Of course, that was all in the past. I thought I knew Rubenstein, but obviously, I did not know him well enough.

It wasn't worth a confrontation, and I looked ahead with some trepidation, but determined to make it on my own.

Chapter 14

On My Own

According to the terms of my contract, I had agreed to practice at least no closer than twenty-five miles from Rubenstein's office. I believed in honoring my word, so I decided I would move out east, into Suffolk County, a bit more rural, and with many more miles to travel between hospitals, most of them smaller than the ones in Nassau County.

Many of the general surgeons at East Nassau Medical Center tried to persuade me to defy Rubenstein and open up in the same town, but I had been a bit intimidated by him. He was too knowledgeable about political in-fighting, and he had a top corporate lawyer advising him. It would obviously be safer for me to move a little out of my way and build up my own practice. I could travel about in the hospitals of eastern Long Island, where I had gathered there was a perpetual shortage of neurosurgeons, and so whenever severe brain injuries or depressed skull fractures occurred, there was a general panic amongst the small hospitals, which try desperately to get a neurosurgeon there, or take a chance and ship the patient by ambulance to one of the major centers to the west, closer to New York City, or even to New York City itself.

Despite the pleas of my colleagues at East Nassau, I eventually resigned from the staff. One of the general surgeons who referred to me as "a class act compared to Rubenstein" had called me on a Saturday night to help him take care of a depressed skull fracture in a ten-year-old child.

It was 5:30 when I saw the lad, and he did need the bone fragments to be "elevated." Kevin Shannon, the general surgeon, knew the situation quite well, and knew there was just Rubenstein and Bloom. He was in fact standing up to Rubenstein, the dictator, by calling me in the first place. He had not received the Rubenstein message, "Don't call Bloom," as yet.

"Bob, I have a depressed fracture here in a ten-year-old. It's an easy case. May I proceed"?

"No, Bill," answered Rubenstein. "Hold on just a minute. This is a frontal fracture, close to the eye, better get an ophthalmological consultation, and you know how parents are with their children these days, better get a plastic surgical consultation also." He knew full well that Saturday night is somewhat difficult to get instant consults. I knew this could not be done and was just an obstacle that Bob set up to make life tough for me. I called him back twenty minutes later and insisted that surgery be done, and that there really was no present need for an ophthalmological and plastic surgery consult.

"What about a pediatric consult? Don't you know that's mandatory on all children?" Rubenstein had me dancing to his tune. Not only did I have to get the pediatric consult, but Kevin Shannon was waiting to help me with the case, as he had done many times before, since he had always preferred me to Rubenstein.

"I'll be there whenever I get there," Rubenstein rudely commented, knowing that Shannon just had to hang around, since I couldn't give him a particular time for starting the surgery. The same applied to the anxious parents of the child. It was now 7:30 on a Saturday evening, and everything depended on Bob Rubenstein, who could take his own sweet time if he wanted to. We had no way of knowing.

At 8:15, Kevin and I were scrubbing up, when Rubenstein

walked in the operating room. "Don't start until I get scrubbed up," he ordered. Rubenstein, the dictator, knew how to make himself a real pain in the butt. I would file a complaint against him for unethical behavior, as a result of this nonsense, but first let's get through with the surgery. Rubenstein took his time with a full ten minute scrub, whistling to himself, as Kevin and I stood helpless in the operating room. The nurse was wondering why we didn't get started. The anesthesiologist, who fully understood the picture here, leaned over and murmured, "You wouldn't want to offend King Robert the Great, would you?"

Rubenstein approached the operating table, picked up the scalpel and said, "Okay Bill, where were you planning to make the incision?"

"I don't plan to make a fresh incision. He already has an incision there, made by the injury itself. I can extend it a couple of centimeters and retract right over the depressed fragments," I replied.

"That's not the way they do it at the Leahy Clinic," Rubenstein retorted disapprovingly.

Rubenstein was totally relentless in his attempts to make me look foolish. I hung in and fought back. "That's all well and good to do it the Leahy Clinic way," I said, "but you do agree it would add an extra half hour of operating time, and we would lose extra blood, not a good idea in a ten-year-old."

"All right, do it your way," Rubenstein relented. At one point, he grabbed the rongeur, a bone cutting instrument, and attempted to "demonstrate" something or other. It was a totally unnecessary act, and I had to remind him that he was only supervising and was not the surgeon. I noticed Kevin was rolling his eyes, fully grasping the battle that was going on between us. He was telling me silently that all I had to do was hang tough, and I could beat Rubenstein at his own game.

It was a little embarrassing when the parents asked me what the delay in the operation was caused by. I couldn't very well tell them the truth without them wondering why they didn't have access to the Chief of Neurosurgery. Since everything went smoothly then and thereafter, it was not a problem.

On Sunday morning, I encountered Kevin in the doctor's cafeteria and told him that I would probably resign from East Nassau, even though I was filing charges of unethical behavior against King Robert the Great. Kevin told me he would take it up with the chief of the surgical department, and that there would be a formal hearing. This took place within the next two weeks. King Robert got a slap on the wrist, but it didn't stop him from harassing me at every opportunity.

Once he called the referring doctor and told him that my management of a case was less than ideal. He would have done it differently, of course. I was tempted to file another charge, but knew it would be equally ineffective. Simply put, Rubenstein had the power, and I didn't.

Many kind souls urged me to stay on the staff, voicing the speculation that sooner or later my influence would be felt, and the chief of surgery would reduce the capacity of Rubenstein to abuse his power. Someone even suggested that the Neurosurgical Department should be abolished entirely, without the semi-independent character of a Neurosurgical Department, and merely let the chief of surgery informally settle any disputes between the two of us. Two other neurosurgeons also practiced at East Nassau, but Rubenstein was successfully discouraging them. Rubenstein's private office was in a prestigious office building, closely connected to the hospital, and he had earlier made sure that I could not plan to have an office there.

Also, he had written to all of the surgeons on the staff, when I became dissociated from him, explaining that he no longer could take any responsibility whatsoever for what Dr. Bloom did in the operating room, suggesting that my work was of inferior quality and should be monitored very carefully.

In my garden at home, I vowed to myself that I would build my own career. Rubenstein was not the only surgeon who abused this power. I would just have to stand up to him and other egomaniacs.

They say that psychiatrists love each other, neurologists tolerate each other and neurosurgeons hate each other. There could certainly be an element of truth in that statement.

Chapter 15

A Long Shot For Rosario Ricci

In my first year of practice, 1962, I received a call from Lakeside Hospital late one Saturday night. This was a small proprietary hospital in Copiague, New York, with about sixty beds. There had been a terrible accident. The worst ones seem to happen at the most ungodly hours of the night.

I arrived to find an 18-year-old boy who had been in a head-on collision with a large truck, only three weeks before graduation from high school. His forehead had been bashed in rather extensively with brain tissue exuding from both sides of his head and blood oozing steadily from the massive wound. Immediate surgery was called for, and I knew it would be an all-night affair, but it would also be Rosario's only chance for survival. In the old days, they would have probably only covered this with a large bandage and waited for the patient to die. Was this patient worth saving with decompressive surgery? Would he end up "a vegetable"? Do we try neurosurgery at this tiny, ill-equipped hospital? I just assumed my best possible attitude.

Had I decided to transfer Rosario to Southside or Good Samaritan Hospitals, which were both better equipped for neurosurgery, we might have risked his life in the process by losing valuable time.

We rushed into the operating room at once, and I quickly dashed to my car where I kept very basic neurosurgical instruments in a bag in the trunk, to be used when a hospital lacked them.

We summoned Clarence, the male operating room nurse on call, the anesthesia department, and Dr. Larry Hornick, a young osteopathic physician on emergency call. We now had a team to attack a very formidable and laborious procedure that faced us.

As we began the surgery at 2 a.m., the Suffolk County Police Department, at our behest, was summoned to take Rosario's blood samples to one of the adjacent hospitals to be cross-matched. Lakeside lacked a blood bank, and the loss of blood from Rosario's injured brain tissue would surely cause him to go into shock within an hour or two. Three units of blood arrived from Brunswick Hospital by 3 a.m., thanks to the cooperation and kindness of the police.

Larry, who had never assisted at a neurosurgical operation, much less seen one, told me he did not feel too well almost two hours into the procedure. I saw he was pale and immediately told him to get out of the room and lie down for a while. Larry found a small stool in the corner of the operating room and sat there for five minutes as I proceeded alone. He kept his hands elevated and sterile, valiantly struggling to fight either nausea or fainting or both.

Larry rejoined me and continued, apologizing for being a weakling. I assured him that there was plenty to be queasy about, as it was now 4 a.m. He had had no sleep, no previous experience in neurosurgery, and had observed nothing but a gory mass of brain and blood for two hours.

At 5:45 a.m., Clarence, the male nurse, yelled, "Doc, please! I hate to have to ask you this, my bladder is killing me!"

"Okay, Clarence, break scrub but don't waste time," I replied. He was back within four or five minutes and, of course, very apologetic. He rescrubbed and returned to action.

And how was the patient doing? Better, I told myself. He's gone from hopeless to terrible to bad. All I have to do is keep my wits about me and maybe we'll get him to "fair" or "stable"—whatever you tell the families or media about how somebody "is doing" in this situation.

At 6:45 a.m., both frontal lobes were decompressed and the lining of the brain had been sutured on both sides. I had removed most of the bone of Rosario's forehead, which would minimize any pressure increase when additional brain swelling occurred. At 7 a.m., the last skin suture was in place and at 7:05, we had completed the dressing. As the surgeon, I also survived but my poor body was asking my mind for help. It had been an awful strain to first make the decision to start the surgery in an unprepared hospital then carry it through to completion. Now I was working on my reserve tank and running out of energy.

Suddenly, I remembered that the hospital's cafeteria opened at 7 a.m., and I nudged Larry, "I think the bacon and eggs should be ready for us about now." Bacon, eggs, and two or three cups of coffee would restore me sufficiently to allow me to talk intelligently to the family, an experience I could not take lightly.

As we passed through the lobby of Lakeside, eighteen members of the Ricci family were gathered there, including Rosario's parents. Everybody wanted to know how he was, and I merely waved my hand and said, "Things are okay, we'll talk to you in just a little while." Larry was visibly upset.

"What's the matter with you?" he said. "You can't talk like that to a family! His life is obviously still in danger, and he's going to have nothing but problems. How can you say what you said?" Larry's brain was fully functional now but mine wasn't!

"Don't worry, Larry. After the bacon, eggs, and coffee, I will be able to speak intelligently with them." And so it was. Larry accompanied me back to the anxious relatives in the lobby. There we spoke kindly but truthfully to the parents. I described what had been done and told them that his chances for survival were good. As for how he would be mentally, it was too early to tell.

In the month that followed, Rosario remained great just by staying alive. His social behavior was not so great. We had expected this to happen with so much loss of brain tissue from both frontal lobes. I called one of Luke Teuber's boys, Steve Chorover, from the Massachusetts Institute of Technology.

The group was still in hot pursuit of people with specific brain injury. Steve flew to Long Island and spent a day or so examining Rosario in great detail. Severe injuries to both frontal lobes result in a lack of social graces, to put it mildly. Rosario could talk and his memory wasn't too horrible. Some minor drawbacks were that he would masturbate in front of the nurses, fling his feces against the wall and would use language that would make a sailor blush.

After a month it was time to discharge him. The nurses were in a state of suppressed glee at the thought of seeing the last of him. In 1962, there were really only two choices for people like Rosario. He could go home with his parents or to go into a state mental hospital. His parents, immigrant Italians, had not the slightest doubt as to where he was going to go—home.

I was relieved that his parents would do the job of rehabilitating Rosario, assuming he could be rehabilitated. You could get good treatment in a hospital, but there you miss the atmosphere of loving, caring parents who are ready to bring you up all over again, as though you were now a baby once more. The same love and care that went into the early years of Rosario's development were now operating all over again. They would change his soiled underwear, feed him, reassure him, defend him from the uncaring world, and protect him from those who would not understand or who might intentionally misunderstand.

Six months later, it was time to provide Rosario with a new forehead. I inserted a metal plate to restore the contour of his skull. The operation went well and it was a great step forward for him. Now when he went out in public he would not attract any negative attention as a result of his sunken forehead.

You might well wonder how Rosario's social behavior was progressing at this point. It was a little better for sure. It wasn't

Dawn Skinner, shown here with the author and her nine-year-old daughter, AlexisJoan. Dawn was the same age when she was considered "hopeless."

AlexisJoan, at age 5, daughter of Dawn Skinner

Sandy Ventrice, one year after nearly being murdered

Breana Raquel Ventrice

Deborah Ribbe, five years after she was considered dead

Coleen Colligan, 12 years following her traumatic paraplegia

New York University-Deparrment of Neurosurgery, 1959. T.I. Hoen (third row, fourth from left) and the author (first row, third from left).

Walter Edward Dandy, the only neurosurgeon nominated for the Nobel Prize, worked at Johns Hopkins throughout his career.

William Herbert Sweet was world renowned for his contributions to the neurosurgical management of pain.

Wallace B. Hamby, Professor of Neurosurgery, University of Buffalo School of Medicine

Sir Geoffrey Jefferson, Dean of British neurosurgeons and founder of the Bristish Neurosurgical Society

The author, at the age of 33, during his tenure as a research fellow in Lund, Sweden

The author as he appeared in the late 1960s

good enough to go out on his own yet. But it was better.

As time went on, I discontinued following Rosario's progress in my office. I had done my job with two operations and all was well in terms of leaving him with a normal-looking skull.

Some years later I learned from a mutual friend that Rosario had done just fine. His high school diploma, missed by three weeks because of the accident, was finally awarded him.

He learned a good trade, made his own living and married. More recently this was verified by Larry Hornick, who still practices in this area. Larry told me that he is without a trace of memory problems and exhibits no anti-social behavior whatsoever. His brain, badly traumatized, somehow adapted. Now someone might say it "rewired" itself.

Was it luck? A miracle? I had done my best as a neurosurgeon, but Rosario's parents had done far more than my surgery. I did not relish their job of taking their son back, with an organic psychosis, perfectly committable as he was. To them, he was their son. They loved him and accepted him regardless of the state he was in.

I salute the parents of Rosario and all parents like them. I congratulate them for what I consider to be the very great triumph of love. Without their supreme effort, I am certain the tedious hours spent in the operating room would have gone for naught.

Not long ago Larry Hornick, still in practice, had a coffee with me and we recalled in detail that fateful, eventful night where only the anesthesiologist was unfazed. Clarence, Larry, and I struggled for hours that morning; the Ricci family struggled for several years afterwards.

Sure, it was a grade B hospital and some could say we were a grade B team, but measured by results I'd say we earned good grades.

Chapter 16

Patricia Walks Again

When I first started practicing neurosurgery in Long Island I felt like the professor coming out into the woods and showing my stuff in the little suburban hospitals of Long Island. These were generally expanding due to the population growth. At Brunswick Hospital in Amityville, New York I had an excellent operating room, thanks to Joseph Epstein, a highly talented senior neurosurgeon, who had maintained a good operating room set-up, with all necessary instruments.

One day I was called to see a twenty-year-old red-headed woman named Patricia, who was steadily losing the use of three of her four limbs. The right arm and leg and the left leg were becoming weaker day by day. She could no longer walk. I performed a cervical myelogram and found a benign tumor at the second cervical level. The tumor was the size and shape of a small plum or a very large olive. I saw no reason why I couldn't remove it right there at Brunswick Hospital. I called one of the surgeons, Kevin Donahue, to assist me, I had used him several times before. Kevin was always gracious and obliging and did his best to help me whenever he could.

I didn't realize that I was in for a big surprise the day that I operated on Patricia. I had placed her on the operating table in the sitting position under general anesthesia and had opened the upper cervical vertebrae. We had exposed the tumor and had been working for about an hour and a half. Kevin looked at the clock, then simply turned to me and said, "Sorry, Bill, I have to leave you right now. I have office hours and I'm already late."

I was so dumbfounded that I could hardly argue with him, but no matter what I said Kevin removed his rubber gloves and gown. There was no stopping him. He headed back to his office.

Ben Leibowitz, the chief of anesthesiology, must have watched the expression on my face as I worked alone to isolate and remove the tumor. He turned the anesthesia over to one of his nursing assistants and left the room. A few minutes later he entered and told me that Armand Prisco, an orthopedic surgeon, was available to help me. About that time the circulating nurse was mopping my brow. I was literally sweating. The fact that Kevin left was part of the reason, but it was also quite a dangerous tumor to remove since we were dealing with the uppermost part of the spinal cord, where any swelling of the cord might interfere with breathing. Both Patricia and I would be in trouble if anything went wrong.

When Dr. Prisco had finished scrubbing and joined me at the operating table, I noticed that I no longer sweated and felt quite a lot more comfortable. I wanted to get the tumor out in one piece and it had to be done without any pressure against the cord and preferably without much bleeding.

Eventually I was able to lift the specimen up and present it to the nurse for submission to pathology. It was a meningioma within the spinal canal. Primary tumors of the spinal canal are often benign and it is the greatest pleasure 'in neurosurgery to reverse what would have gone on to complete paraplegia or, in Patricia's case, quadriplegia, eventual respiratory paralysis and death. A few months later Patricia was walking and within six months she had regained all her lost spinal cord function. I followed her progress for another ten years and, although she moved away to Connecticut, she liked to see me from time to time. The feeling was mutual. She married and had children, somehow adding to my personal sense of gratification.

Dr. Prisco and I, both retired from surgical practice, see each other often and laugh at the incident in retrospect. I remind him that I as never so glad to see a "voluntary" assistant in the operating room, and he reminds me he was just doing his duty as a compassionate doctor.

As for Kevin Donahue, I was always polite and cordial to him, but never called on him to assist me thereafter. If I had been removing a hemorrhoid or a tonsil on Patricia, I could understand his behavior and excuse it. I can't figure out whether Kevin thought he was simply not needed or that I was so experienced I could do without him in the first place.

Another case of spinal cord compression at Brunswick Hospital by tumor involved a nun who was losing the use of her legs and had just become bedridden. I removed a walnut-sized neurofibroma, another benign tumor of the spinal canal, from the middle of her spine. Again, it was pure gratification to watch her regain function of her legs day by day, and walk out of the hospital within three weeks. Two or three months post-operatively she told me that she played tennis with her niece and it was about that time that I decided that she did not need to continue to be followed by me. Usually these benign tumors, whether they are meningiomas or neurofibromas, can be removed completely, with the result so sweet and satisfying. If I could limit my neurosurgical practice I would limit it to benign tumors of the spinal canal and chronic subdural hematomas of the intracranial cavity, but when one does general neurosurgery this kind of thinking remains a dream.

Speaking of nuns, I find them to be the most motivated to get well of any group that I have operated on. They are absolutely dedicated to doing good things with their lives and that same motivation seems to propel them forward when it comes to taking good care of themselves. Certainly I find they follow doctor's orders to a tee. In my next life I will probably limit my practice to nuns with neurosurgical problems.

Chapter 17

Subdural Hematoma—Trouble for All Ages

In 1963, I presented a scientific paper in Minneapolis at the American Academy of Neurology Meeting on subdural hematoma in infants and children, and later showed similar material at the Congress of Neurological Surgeons meeting in Denver. It attracted some attention, because it contributed to prevention of mental retardation by promoting the proper diagnosis of subdural hematoma in infants, a treatable and curable condition. We might say that pediatric neurology and neurosurgery were fairly young at that time.

At Hospital for Sick Children in London, I had worked with Kenneth Till, another McKissock associate, studying subdural fluid collections in babies, which are markedly different from those in adults. Some of these collections are clear fluid rather than blood, but there are varying combinations. Standard operating procedure was to put a needle in the baby's head and withdraw no more than 20 cc (two-thirds of an ounce) of fluid per day. I felt that the heads of these babies was inflated a little bit like a balloon, and the sustained pressure on the brain was damaging. Why not withdraw as much fluid as is necessary to reduce the pressure to normal? Would not this prevent damage and save some of the babies from a needless major operation?

At Southside Hospital in 1963, I removed, with a single aspiration, 4½ ounces of bloody fluid from the enlarged head of an infant, and on the following day, removed three ounces additionally. This flouted standard procedure, of course, but with great results. The baby left the hospital without need for surgery since, on the third day, there seemed to be no fluid left.

I was quite sure I was on to an improved technique for dealing with subdural collections, but I didn't feel confident enough to rebut the Boston Brahmins, Ingraham and Matson, authors of a standard textbook in pediatric neurosurgery. Then, I talked to William Collins who, at Western Reserve in Cleveland, had done some research on subdurals. He told me it cannot be reproduced in an animal model, and that he, too, felt that one could remove large quantities of fluid from babies' heads without danger and with beneficial results. Babies with large heads do not necessarily have hydrocephalus; it can turn out to be a subdural fluid collection. Nowadays, of course, the scans give us an immediate diagnosis. Truly, we have come a long way in our understanding of subdural hematomas and related problems. Collins, incidentally, went on to become Chairman of the Department of Neurosurgery at Yale.

Before leaving the subject, it should be noted that elderly people present a different problem. Their brains are not like rubber balls that have been indented by the overlying clot, re-expanding to their normal contour when the clot is removed. Elderly brains are more like mudpies, where pressure over a period of time leaves the brain indented. It doesn't re-expand like young brains. Therefore, it is better to use a craniectomy, a technique for simply removing bone and not replacing it. This leaves a deformity of the scalp, forming a concavity, but it tends to eliminate other problems, such as recurrent bleeding. At a later stage, the cosmetic deformity can be repaired. I learned too that using a syringe and needle can often prevent extra operations in the elderly. By aspirating through the area of missing bone, we can simply remove subdural material. Neurosurgeons quite properly look for new conditions to operate upon. Only those who are also good doctors try to prevent unnecessary surgery.

When subdural hematomas are acute, as is often the case with boxers who get knocked out after repeated blows to the head, there is an extremely high mortality. Every year, it seems that at least one boxer dies of the brain injury associated with acute subdural hematoma, and the surgery in this situation is seemingly of little or no value. It isn't the blood clot that kills so much as the repeated blows to the head, and the resultant brain swelling.

Recently, Mike Tyson knocked out a man in just half a minute, whereby the first blow to the head stunned him. The referee wisely spotted the man as "concussed," and in danger of serious brain injury as Iron Mike pummelled away. The ref himself was floored in the process of protecting the victim, who could easily have died with one more solid blow to the head.

Some of the audience may have been unhappy with the ref's actions. How mournful would they be if the fighter was "put to sleep" permanently?

The ref was absolutely correct in stopping the fight, however early, and whether or not the audience got "their money's worth." The many dead fighters, the Parkinsonism of Mohammed Ali, the "punch drunk" fighters of the early twentieth century—all are testimony that the brain is a delicate organ, able to withstand only a very limited battering by repeated blows to the head.

Chapter 18

The Toughest Night And The Longest Day

I often think about what has tested my physical and moral fiber most, and always arrive at the same conclusion. It wasn't the Rosario Ricci case—it was my night of triage.

To compound the matter, it was the night that our hired man died. My wife and I were in bed, about to go to sleep, at 1 a.m., when we received the call that our adopted schizophrenic patient, Rudolph, whom we took into our home as a man-servant, had died. We talked about Rudolph's funeral. It would have to be organized by us and we would, of course, have to inform his relatives.

At about 2 a.m., there was an emergency call from Good Samaritan Hospital, informing me that there was a bad head injury that needed my services. Dressing quickly, I hastened to the emergency room where, lo and behold, there was not one, but a total of three serious brain injuries. There was no other neurosurgeon on call or even reachable. The situation was dumped into my lap.

I had to carry out triage, selecting which would be operated on first. It just so happened that all three head injuries required emergency surgery. One was a depressed skull fracture that penetrated the brain lining, another was an acute subdural hematoma that required surgical drainage, the third was a severe head injury, mainly with edema, but also with a developing clot.

It was quite obvious to me that since the third man had the least likelihood of survival, he would be scheduled last. I would start my first operation at 2:30 a.m., without benefit of an assistant. I had deliberately trained myself to be able to do some of the simple emergency procedures, simple for a neurosurgeon with sufficient experience, knowing that the scrub nurse could do procedures that normally are assigned to the assistant. I knew it would save a half hour or so of operating time, and I was fortunate in having an expert scrub nurse who had worked with me many times before. She touched my forceps with the cautery, gently, so as not to move my forceps, the tips of which held tiny little vessels on the surface of the brain and the dura, the main lining membrane. I chose the patient with the depressed fracture compressing the motor strip of the brain to be first since he had seizures and although we were able to control them medically with intravenous valium and dilantin, I felt that prolonged pressure of the depressed fragment would be detrimental.

The second patient had some venous blood under the dura that needed evacuation, but he had been stable for some time in the emergency room, about 45 minutes or so, before I made my decision to put him in the number two spot. I finished my first procedure within two hours and by 5 a.m., I had the second patient wheeled in.

I drained the subdural hematoma and left a modest decompression in the bone, a procedure called a craniectomy, whereby the burr hole is enlarged to a diameter of one-and-a half to two inches or more. This, I also did without an assistant, and finished in about two hours or so. Now that we were past 7 a.m., it was easier to get an assistant.

For the third procedure, a smaller subdural collection with a patient that, on postmortem examination, proved to have massive edema. I apparently picked my triage well, since the last man to be operated on had the least chance of survival, yet deserved to have some opportunity for survival that surgical decompression offered. This was a larger decompression than my second triage patient, since he had considerable swelling of brain tissues underneath the blood collection and needed a three and one-half inch diameter bony decompression. Despite this, massive doses of pressure-reducing agents and hyperventilation, he seemed to be a lost cause.

Like my first triage patient, he had been a participant in a bar room brawl and had been clubbed with a baseball bat several times. Multiple severe blows to the head are more dangerous than the effects of a single blow, and this is why one or two boxers die of acute subdural hematoma every year.

At 11:15 a.m., I called my secretary to get multiple messages, staggered to my car, and, with two or three cups of black coffee coursing through my system , was able to drive out to Riverhead where I had committed myself to give testimony in a court case. I was stretching myself, even though I was in my mid-40s, the exciting night without a moment of sleep had me feel lucky that I had not driven off the road, even with my caffeine jag. I managed to get through the court case that afternoon and at 5 p.m., staggered, almost unseeing, into the parking lot and drove the 45 minutes back home to Bay Shore. How wonderful it would feel to flop into bed. I prayed that this would be the case since I had absolutely no reserves if I were needed once more.

Barbara, my wife, informed me that it was unfortunate that they couldn't get me in the courtroom because there was another emergency at Brookhaven Hospital in Patchogue, Long Island, that required my services—bullet wound to the spine with partial paralysis.

Since the only other neurosurgeon capable of operating at Brookhaven Hospital was out of town that particular day, I had no choice.

This was a double emergency. The victim of the bullet wound needed a neurosurgeon. The neurosurgeon needed another neurosurgeon to replace him, but didn't have one. I didn't even have the strength to drive back to Brookhaven Hospital, much less operate. Barbara quickly got the picture and called on a dear friend, who was also employed as my landscaper from time to time. He was kind enough to come to the house and chauffeur me to the hospital. This provided me with twenty-five minutes of blissful sleep in the back of the car.

When we got to the hospital, I was now on my second set of reserves. It seemed as though I had no choice. I had to somehow summon up the energy. I had two more cups of black coffee at this point, and later wondered whether I had a tremor from coffee nerves when I operated.

This time a general surgeon, Steve Green, helped me. As in triage case number three the patter of conversation between me and the general surgeon assisting me kept me fully alert throughout the procedure. Although the prime object was not to remove the bullet from the spinal canal, but rather to decompress the spinal cord of bone fragments and a small amount of blood clot.

I learned in five minutes how the new metal detector functioned and put it to use. I had never used this in the spine or the brain. It was the first time. I was able to locate the bullet with relative ease using this machine, which made the Suffolk Police very happy. They seemed to be thrilled to receive the missile. They had waited and were now outside the operating room. I didn't bother to mention to my assistant or the nurses that I had been up all night. I am pleased to report, the patient eventually improved after the surgery!

As soon as I returned to Joe DiMarco's Buick, I flopped on the back seat with just a few short words to Joe, and immediately sank into a truly blissful sleep, which was again rudely and startlingly terminated with Joe half-dragging me out of the car. I literally staggered into the house, where Barbara had my bed opened and ready for me.

She even had a cup of warm cocoa with milk to soothe my stomach and possibly my overwrought nervous system. Although, at this point, I wouldn't dare describe my nervous system, I seemed to do everything right from 2 a.m., as my work day started, until 10 p.m., when my work day ended, having done three major brain operations and one major spinal cord operation, all of them serious emergencies.

I have ruminated about this many times and believe that this is what I would call, "the longest day" that I have ever experienced. That I was able to help three out of four and operate twice without an assistant and drive nearly two hours without an accident only proves that one has to be full of toughness and determination.

Not long ago, a teenage girl, admitted to a hospital through the emergency ward was assigned a bed where she died shortly thereafter. A highly publicized lawsuit followed initiated by her father, a prominent journalist. The New York State legislature, as a reaction to the notoriety of the case, passed laws that are supposed to guarantee that hospital doctors-in-training receive a sufficient amount of sleep to conduct their duties. The new statutes, largely ignored, are known as the Libby Zion laws in medical and hospital parlance. The Libby Zion laws are, in my opinion, rather unwarranted. Had I not had similar experiences back in my training days? Once I spent twenty out of twenty-four hours in the Bellevue operating room doing six operations when I was chief resident.

The body and the spirit adapt to stressful situations. There is little doubt that, had the Libby Zion laws been on the books during my training I could not have helped more than one of the first three cases. Someone, or maybe two, would have died or remained paraplegic had I been pampered by having plenty of regular sleep in my residency. I surely would not have been up to what I did.

Chapter 19

The Re-Creation of Linda Drake

It was early 1964 when Barbara and I became comfortably ensconced in our new Long Island home overlooking the Great South Bay. The village, or hamlet, as it was technically called, was Bay Shore, known to hoards of Manhattanites as the place to catch the Fire Island ferry. One reason we picked the house was that it was only one mile from Southside Hospital, a primary hospital for performing neurosurgery, especially since I would be on call every other day and every other weekend.

One night a phone call came. "Dr. Bloom, we need you in the emergency room, we have a case of status epilepticus?" That is the term for repeated convulsions that stop only momentarily. There is at least a fifty percent chance of mortality, I thought, and after telling the emergency room physician to squirt a couple of grains of phenobarbital into the patient's vein, I was on my way to the emergency room. I arrived within two minutes. The intravenous barbiturate was just completed, and the convulsions would soon slow down somewhat.

The patient was Linda Drake, a seventeen-year-old mother of a little baby girl. Her husband was only two years older than she was, and he was in a very excited state.

"I didn't know what to do", he said, " 'cause we didn't have a phone in our house. All I kept doing was counting her convulsions. When it got to eighty, I decided she might die." I was glad he figured that out.

"So, I ran to the nearest house where there was a phone to call an ambulance," he continued.

I estimated the total number of seizures probably exceeded a hundred. Not that the number mattered exactly, but previously I had never seen more than about twenty. I wondered if Linda would be alive within one hour, one week, one year, five years? My little reverie ended when I became conscious of her breathing difficulty. She was turning blue.

"Shall we call the anesthesia department to intubate?" asked the ER doctor.

"No, just give me a trach set," I replied. "We're better off that way." Linda was about to die from insufficient oxygen and choking on her own mucus secretions.

Within seconds, the nurse pushed a tracheotomy set before me. I quickly dabbed a disinfectant solution on her neck, infiltrated the skin with novocaine, and cut the skin down to her windpipe just above her Adam's apple. I cut out a piece of cartilage and slipped the slightly C-shaped metal curved tube down the trachea. She could now be suctioned out. Her skin changed color to pink almost immediately, indicating she was now getting enough oxygen. With the tracheotomy tube in place, we could now give her all the phenobarbital we needed to, even if we had to approach toxic doses.

We had saved her from death by choking on her own secretions. Now we had to save her from death due to the persistent convulsions by giving her large doses of intravenous medications even if it was necessary to keep her in a prolonged coma.

It was Linda's mother who was the mature member of the family. She was about thirty-eight-years-old, one of the real young grandmothers. She bore Linda while still very young, and Linda had her baby at seventeen.

When Linda's convulsions finally ceased and she emerged from the coma, I could then evaluate her. A week elapsed, and it appeared that she had cerebral palsy. Her right limbs were tight, shrunken and contracted. She could use her right hand very poorly, and she could walk only with a pronounced limp, obviously favoring her right leg, which, like her right arm, was also atrophied. Her mother verified this had been the case since Linda's birth.

Immediately, I began to think of a hemispherectomy. Yes, Linda would be the perfect candidate for removing the left half of her brain. It would help her mental status, her seizure problem, and would be precisely what she needed, assuming, of course, that she was blind in the right field of vision and insensitive to normal sensory phenomena on the right side of her body. That removing most of a cerebral hemisphere can result in a miraculous improvement may be hard to believe. Every so often it is presented as a new discovery. In London, I saw half a dozen such cases that Wylie McKissock had operated on, talked to the mothers and examined the patients themselves. A South African neurosurgeon devised this operation years previously. The results were miraculous.

When I was able to test her visual field and sensory phenomena on the right side, I found they were normal. That meant we could not take out the left half of her brain, since we would create a deficit in the sensory and visual fields on the right side, even though we would relieve the seizures and behavior problems. So much for that idea. First, do no harm. We had to pursue another course, obviously.

I followed Linda's progress after her discharge from the hospital and carefully regulated her phenobarbital and dilantin doses. She needed goodly amounts of both. The dilantin, of course, made her less groggy and made it possible to use less phenobarbital. She was able to walk and limp around in her usual fashion for quite some time, having only occasional mild seizures. Naturally, I had to be prepared for what happened if she went into status again or if some other strange thing happened to her. What an unfortunate figure she was—trying to care for a baby, having seizures, limping around, being driven everywhere. She looked to me for guidance, and I gave it to her, usually in the presence of her mother, rather than her husband.

Another year went by, and I was informed that she had divorced her husband. There were now three females in the household—grandmother, mother, and baby.

Linda was free from marital strife and stress, without which she seemed to thrive. She took small amounts of dilantin, no phenobarbital.

But I was wrong about the thriving. Another emergency call at Southside. It was Linda. She had attempted suicide by overdosing. Life, even without her husband, was simply too overwhelming.

I was ready for this one. I had spent much time conferring with others, especially Joe Ransohoff, a neurosurgeon for whom I have always had enormous respect. Joe agreed that a left temporal lobectomy was more appropriate than the more radical hemispherectomy, but it ought to be undertaken only at a propitious moment. Now the moment had arrived, I decided. We were ready for the heroic measures.

First, I had a long talk with Linda's mother about her future, her unfortunate crippling brain problem, and what I thought the temporal lobectomy would accomplish. We would remove the front two inches or so of the temporal lobe of the left side of her brain, including the amygdala and hippocampus (Greek names for almond and seahorse). I then had to persuade Linda, who was understandably nervous, to have part of her brain removed. Strangely, the hair removal bothered her more than the removal of brain tissue.

The next day, I spent some time with Linda and presented her with a blonde wig which I'd purchased for $65.00. This moved her. I never did this for any other of the 2000 heads I have shaved prior to brain surgery during the course of my career.

Linda decided she would go through with it. First, I transferred her to Central Islip Psychiatric Hospital, a New York

State Institution where I was chief of both the neurology and neurosurgery departments. Everything was set up for a left temporal lobectomy. I briefly wondered whether our facilities were adequate for this "advanced" neurosurgical procedure.

My thoughts took me back to the operating room of the Serafimer Hospital in Stockholm, Sweden. It was March 1960, and I was watching Dr. Herbert Olivacrona, Europe's greatest neurosurgeon, performing a left temporal lobectomy for temporal lobe epilepsy. There were five neurophysiologists assisting in recording brain waves from various parts of the exposed brain, interpreting and recording data.

"How does what they find influence the surgery?" I asked Olivacrona's assistant, Dr. Boehm.

"It doesn't have any influence whatsoever," Boehm replied. "He lets them have their fun, then he lops off the temporal lobe in the same old way."

Let me explain Boehm's use of the term, "lops off." He meant "excision." It did not imply a casual act or a quick removal. It was just Boehm's humorous way of explaining a routine temporal lobe resection.

Now, in Central Islip Hospital's operating room, we had no neurophysiologists although I had given our research department a chance to participate.

A psychiatrist with surgical experience assisted me both with the surgery and the subsequent paper we published about Linda.

Eventually, we had removed the anterior two and a quarter inches of Linda's temporal lobe, including, I fervently hoped, her left almond and seahorse. Without removing these structures, the operation could have been be a failure. I used a number of metal clips as markers and post-operative x-rays proved that we had indeed excised these critical structures of her limbic system.

Linda's operation proved to be an even bigger success than we had hoped for. The day after surgery, we cut her phenobarbital dose down from six grains daily to a half a grain. The next day, we eliminated all anti-convulsants. Linda became alert, sharper than she had been in many years, and she appeared happier than I had ever known her to be. Her mother reported that her right limbs were less spastic. She walked better and her handwriting had greatly improved. She was soon out of the hospital and living with her mother and daughter, Sherry.

For several years, Sherry and my own daughter Deborah were classmates in school. Eventually they learned of the doctor/patient relationship of their respective parents.

And how did Linda do for the next 15 years? Just fine. She came off welfare, obtained a steady job, supported Sherry until she grew up and married.

And in 1988, when Morris Loffman, my dearest friend in neurosurgery, came from California visiting with his wife, Sonia, we drove to the tip of a waterfront pier in Bay Shore, New York, and parked. By sheer coincidence Linda was in the next car. We spotted each other at the same time, leaped out of our cars and embraced warmly.

It did my heart good, not having seen her in years, to learn how well she and her family were doing, and to be congratulated by Morris on my "result." In fact, Linda herself had become a grandmother, and showed pictures to prove it.

Not bad, I thought, considering that when I first saw her, her chances of surviving a single day were very questionable at best.

Chapter 20

The Vegetable We Sent To Credemore
(The Robert Adler Story)

In 1965, I received an emergeny call from the Central General Hospital Emergency Room in Plainview, Long Island. I had been on staff there only a short time. A 17-year-old boy had been struck by a car, and as a result, was now suffering a serious closed-head injury. He was in a deep coma so they urged me to come quickly?

I arrived at the emergency room to find the boy breathing very poorly. He had just begun to turn blue, as a result of choking on his secretions. There was no time to waste. I had to do a tracheotomy by myself. As I suctioned the mucus, his color went from blue to pink.

Now it was time to admit him to the new intensive care unit which had just become available that day. Robert Adler was the first actual patient admitted. The red-headed charge nurse asked for very specific instructions, and I discussed at length what she should look for.

"Check pulse, respiration, and blood pressure every half hour. Have a catheter placed and report any excessive urinary output. Suction the trach tube whenever he needs it and get the medical men to check out his chest every so often." We did not have chest specialists in those days.

Robert developed just about every complication associated

with severe head injuries. First, it was excessive water output (diabetes insipidus), which we controlled with a medication called pitressin. Then it was seizures, which were quickly controlled with the usual anti-convulsants. His increased intracranial pressure was largely controlled with steroids. It was necessary for me to do a study of his blood vessels (angiogram) to make sure he did not have an intracranial clot. He didn't, but we had to find out just the same. He had urinary infection and lung problems, but these were handled one at a time.

We closed off his tracheotomy tube and ultimately removed the device. He breathed well on his own. We had to turn him frequently to prevent bed sores. The right side of his body was partially paralyzed from the brain injury. He was unable to speak or communicate in any other fashion. At six weeks, I pinched him to see if he would talk or respond. All we got was an animal-like howl, a pathetic and pitiful response to a stimulus.

I spoke frankly with the boy's distraught mother who lived in Queens. She had no money, and there were no rehabilitation centers in those days. It was obvious to both of us that he couldn't be cared for at home. The only alternative was a state mental hospital. I made the arrangements for the transfer to Credemore Psychiatric State Hospital in Queens, New York, reasonably close to the mother. Within a year, Robert was only a memory and after another year, the memory had faded almost entirely.

During evening office hours two years later, I was approached by a dapper young man. He was very nattily dressed, sporting a clean shirt, tie, and sport jacket. He was clean-shaven and looked recently groomed.

"You probably won't remember me, Dr. Bloom," he said. "My name is Robert Adler, and you took care of me two years ago. I don't remember you at all, sir, but I understand you helped me quite a bit, and I wanted to come and thank you for what you have done." My eyes must have filled with tears of joy as I realized who he was and what progress he had made.

"My goodness, now I recall you! What are you doing these

days?" I asked.

"I'm a college student. I've finished my freshman year, and I am majoring in science courses."

My last memory of this boy was his primal scream when I pinched him. When I think back of how hard we labored to pull this young man through his many complications, I swelled with pride and a sense of glory and achievement. It reminded me never to give up and to utilize every method at my disposal to give each patient a chance at recovery, a chance to realize their life's dreams.

I bid Robert farewell and wished him luck. It wasn't necessary for me to follow him at this point, but as the years went by, I occasionally wondered just how far Robert progressed.

Eight more years elapsed and I had a new patient who was vaguely familiar to me. It was the same red-headed nurse that had taken care of Robert. She came to me with a peripheral nerve problem that she had developed. After dispensing some advice we began talking about the first patient to be admitted to the Central General Hospital Intensive Care Unit. "I wonder how Robert Adler is these days," I asked.

"Well, I'll tell you," the nurse replied. "We write to each other regularly. In fact, I have a picture of him here with me. He's married, has three children, lives in California, and is a computer expert. Not bad for the vegetable that we sent out to Credemore".

We reveled in the joint glory of our achievements. We realized that if it were not for the intensive care unit, Robert would not be alive today. The intensive care unit opened in the nick of time for Robert! I've seen a few patients who expired that could not be handled in ordinary hospital units, since they were simply not prepared for the urgent complications of severe head injuries. Robert could have died from any of five or six different causes. He was fortunate to have survived them all and then to make the most of his life, as he has done.

Of course, all of society benefits by the steady advances of medicine in general, as well as in neurosurgery. Oftentimes, it seems that society today takes seminal achievements too much for granted. The miracles of yesterday are the routine events of today.

Chapter 21

Surprise, Surprise

Neurosurgery can be depressing at times. We like to think we're tough enough to handle anything, any situation. It helps to be able to pass from one mood to another instantly. Only once did I need alcohol to change moods. It was at my 39th birthday party when I drank a full glass of vodka to slip from the depths of despair into a proper party mood.

My friend Robert Blossom was under strict instructions from my wife to keep me away from my home until the 50 or so guests arrived for the surprise party. Bob chauffeured me around and when I was beeped for an emergency at Mid Island Hospital in Bethpage, he volunteered to drive me there to see a seventeen-year-old boy with a cut on his eyelid from a sledding accident at Bethpage State Park. The eye doctor said that he was worried because the boy was sleepy and had a headache.

The victim was virtually lobotomized by a sled runner that passed just above his right eye, through the thin bone that forms the roof of the eye socket and through a major artery supplying the right frontal lobe of the brain.

When the boy arrived at the emergency room, all he had externally was a half inch cut on the right eyelid. It wasn't even bleeding. Even the x-ray didn't show much. But it did show a tiny piece of bone penetrating the brain like a knife or a bullet would have caused, a tell-tale clue.

I rushed him to the operating table as fast as was possible and carried out the surgery expeditiously. I found the right frontal lobe of his brain to be a mass of blood clot and dead brain under great pressure, but by the time I found the bleeding artery and dealt with it, he was already brain dead.

The mother, had been patiently waiting for me and stood up, initiating the conversation with, "Will his eye be all right?"

I told her what happened and that, somehow, God only knows, the runner of the sled didn't damage the eye but kept going through the skull bone and into the brain, tearing the largest artery during the process. "I'm sorry I didn't take time out to call you, but I did exactly what I would have wanted a doctor to do if I were the patient."

Then she asked me if I would be kind enough to explain to her husband what had happened to their only child.

"My husband just got out of the hospital a few days ago from a heart attack. It would be better, doctor, if you explained things to him."

My God, how gentle can I be? "Your son had a sled runner sever his anterior cerebral artery, and he bled to death while I tried to fix things and failed!" What could I say?

By the time I had finished my sad chore, I wanted to cry. Bob drove me home silently, sensing my need to be alone with my thoughts.

Why are all those cars in my driveway? They're all over the street. My God! It's my birthday, is it a surprise party?

Entering the house ahead of Bob, it was "SURPRISE, SURPRISE!" Everyone was toasting with their glasses raised. I was two hours late.

"Sit down and be the sultan. Barbara hired a belly dancer. Where were you?" someone said. "The dancer and the musician have to do their thing and get back to New York City."

It was at that moment I quietly poured vodka into a water glass and chug-a-lugged it. It took effect in two minutes and was enough so I could pretend to enjoy my 39th birthday party.

I did what a sultan was supposed to do, eye the belly dancer, nod, and smile. I had turned off the scenario of my failed surgical effort.

I must absolutely advise the reader not to emulate me with the treatment of the glass of vodka poured down the throat in that manner. Unless perhaps, you happen to have a similar experience.

Chapter 22

A Happy Mistake

Saturday nights are when most people are enjoying themselves, while I would remain alcohol-free and await the outcome of auto accidents, bar-room brawls, and family disputes.

This Saturday was no different when the phone rang. It was the staff of the emergency room at Good Samaritan Hospital calling.

"Dr. Bloom, we have a skull fracture in an elderly lady; she's semi-comatose, and her vital signs are stable."

"I'll be right there!"

I leaped into my car. Ten minutes later, in the emergency room, I checked the x-rays and verified a skull fracture in the right temporal bone. She moaned when I pinched her and moved her arms. Her scalp was swollen over the fracture site.

Her husband explained that he had found her at the foot of the stairs. It seemed to be a clear-cut case of trauma, and I wrote the usual orders for the intensive care nurses to follow. I also requested a medical man to check her over carefully for any possible condition that needed treatment. I hopped in my car and went to sleep as soon as I got home. It was well after midnight. Actually, I expected to receive some sort of call on this lady during the night from intensive care, considering the amount of brain injury. This was in the 1960s, prior to CT or

MRI scans. We generally waited for a worsening of the neurological condition to occur. Should this happen, we would then rush the patient to the x-ray department for an angiogram, a study of the blood vessels, or directly to the operating room on occasion, if the deterioration was rapid and followed a certain pattern.

As it turned out, there were no calls. By 10 the next morning, as I drove to Good Samaritan Hospital, I wondered if this lady could have died during the night without someone calling me.

That was unlikely, I thought, since I was the doctor of record, and the rules are that I must be called. Of course, someone could have made a mistake and called the medical man instead, and he could have pronounced her dead during the night. On the other hand, she may have had a severe brain bruise from which she was slowly but steadily recovering.

Well, no sense thinking about it, I'll find out soon enough. I parked my car and trudged into the hospital, climbed the stairs and entered the intensive care unit.

First, I gazed into the room where my patient was supposed to be. There was a lady sitting upright in bed conversing with her family, drinking a glass of water. I checked the chart very carefully to make sure I had the right person.

I couldn't believe my eyes and checked again to make sure, even asking the nurse if I had the right patient. It simply did not make sense for an elderly brain injured person to recover so rapidly.

Hiding my quizzical expression, I breezed into her room, shook the lady's hand, and said, "My, you certainly recovered fast, you must be made of good stuff." She responded in a perfectly oriented and conversational manner, though with a period of amnesia for the event. I turned to her husband and asked, "Now let's see, you found her at the foot of the stairs?" He nodded rather slowly with an apathetic expression on his face. I left the room, still hiding my confusion.

Suddenly, their teenage son caught up with me, following me toward the desk. "You doctors like to have all the information, right?"

"Information certainly is useful when it is available," I replied, still sorting out my thoughts.

"Well, I think you should know what happened last night. You see, uh, my mother hanged herself, and my father found her and cut the rope with a knife. He couldn't catch her as she fell, and her head hit the floor quite hard."

I thanked the young boy for this information and sat down at the desk. My disorientation gradually cleared.

Of course, I hadn't checked her neck for rope burns. No one had told me that she hanged herself, and nobody in the emergency room had noticed rope burns. If they were there, we all missed it. I attributed her entire condition to trauma, when in fact she had been asphyxiated by the process of hanging. These are very different matters. Her brain had suffered from lack of oxygen for a period of time, and that was more responsible for her condition than the skull fracture injury. The trauma, even though it caused the skull fracture, was not serious. Cerebral anoxia is far more reversible than a traumatic condition of the brain, all other factors being equal.

Well, we all missed the diagnosis here, but who cares? This was a happy ending and that's what counts. Coexisting oxygen deprivation can always make the situation seem worse in any case of trauma.

Of course, it would have been nice if her husband had related the true story when she arrived at the hospital. It doesn't always apply, perhaps, but when things are really serious it's better for the family or the patient to reveal the truth.

Concerning the "happy ending," I obviously am referring only to the patient's brain and not her mind. She had to have been severely troubled to attempt suicide by hanging. I did not release her until a psychiatrist saw her and arranged for follow-up care. Strange as it may seem the brain injury produced amnesia and erased the memory of her suicide attempt.

Was the brain injury a blessing in disguise? Don't try to answer that one!

Chapter 23

It's Hard To Kill A Newfoundlander
(Story Of Alice McNeil)

In 1970, Joseph Kennedy, an eye doctor, called in a concerned voice. "Bill, I have a thirty-six-year-old Canadian woman with pain behind her eyes."

He thought there might be a slight visual field defect due to something going on in the brain. Of course, I wanted to check the woman out immediately.

The woman was working in a decorator's studio in my own town of Bay Shore, and she spoke with a Newfoundland accent. I discovered that she had hallucinations of odor. She smelled foul odors that did not exist. At times, this is a sign of temporal lobe tumor, and has to be taken very seriously. I also noted there was some drooping of the left side of her mouth and that her headache was somewhat worse on the right than the left. This combination of symptoms suggested that she could very well have a brain tumor in the right temporal region.

I admitted her immediately to Southside Hospital and carried out an angiogram. CT Scans and MRI's had not yet been invented. The angiogram verified that there was indeed a mass in the right temporal lobe. It did not have the characteristics of a highly malignant primary brain tumor, yet the likelihood was overwhelming that it was a primary brain tumor. There was no sign of cancer anywhere in this woman's body.

One thing I noticed about Alice was that she seemed to be fearless when I told her of the possibilities and the fact that we needed to get into the right side of her brain and biopsy or remove tissue. She didn't cry or show any signs of nerves. She discussed it with her husband as I did, and upon mutual agreement, we took her to the operating room. Dr. Altchek, another neurosurgeon, assisted me, and we palpated tissue within the right temporal lobe that appeared to be abnormal. It was somewhat firmer than usual. We were careful not to go too far back to avoid making her worse visually. I must say I was a bit shocked when the pathology report showed no clear evidence of tumor. This meant going before a committee and explaining myself.

Had we missed the tumor? Perhaps we removed tumor, but the pathology department examined a different portion of it? This, and other thoughts came to mind when I had to face the committee. That's the way it should be. Naturally, I was concerned. The chief of surgery, the chief of radiology and several other important physicians were there to await my explanation of why we didn't find what we were supposed to find. Was it a misdiagnosis?

Dr. Arthur Drazan, a radiologist, immediately came to my rescue. "There is no question that there is a brain tumor here," he clearly stated. "The angiogram shows it," he said, as he demonstrated the findings on the films shown. The fact that her mouth no longer drooped on the left side showed that we had produced an adequate decompression.

In the next year or so, she gradually developed a complete blindness in the left field of vision. This is not blindness in the left eye. With either eye closed, she was blind in the left half of her visual field. Now that she was totally blind in the left visual field (owing to the natural progression of the tumor). It was dangerous for her to drive. People who have this so-called homonymous hemianopsia tend to bump into things on the blind side. This is obviously dangerous but patients are often not warned of it. Alice once caught herself driving on the wrong side of the road and was smart enough to stop driving.

We prepared for a second operation at Southside Hospital. Dr. R.J. Seymour assisted me. This time I was unafraid of entering the visual field area since the tumor had already destroyed the visual function. We removed as much tissue as we could safely remove. I checked the pathology myself with Southside Hospital's pathologist, and we both diagnosed it as astrocytoma, a star cell tumor. It was what we had suspected all along.

Just to be even more sure of ourselves, we sent the histologic slides to Dr. Harry Zimmerman at Montefiore Hospital. Dr. Zimmerman, as one professor of neurosurgery phrased it, was the "Joe DiMaggio of neuropathology" at that time, one of the world's very best. He verified that it was indeed a low grade astrocytoma and suggested that she receive radiation therapy. That was precisely what I had in mind, but felt reassured by his expert opinion. Without an exact diagnosis, our radiation therapy department would not proceed.

I continued to follow Alice's progress for another three years. She kept working in the decorator's studio on Main Street. Then she told me that she was heading back to Newfoundland with her husband. She wanted to spend what remained of her life in her home town of Port-aux-Basques. I expected that Alice could possibly survive another few years, but that her husband would become a widower.

In 1992, some seventeen years later, I received a call from Newfoundland. Sure enough, it was Alice. "What! You're still alive?" was the first thing that crossed my mind. Of course, I didn't mention this to Alice.

"I want to come for a check up, Dr. Bloom, if I may. I want to know how I'm doing. I've had a few headaches lately."

"Absolutely," I responded. "We'll be ready for you whenever you arrive."

When Alice came to Long Island, I ordered an MRI, now

that we had this test available. It showed no tumor, just the effects of radiation. I was glad to tell her that she was the longest survivor of a brain tumor that I had ever personally had. In fact, I told her, she might even be some sort of record. There is no way of knowing, but I would research it.

The following summer, I came to Nova Scotia on a fishing trip with a friend, Dr. Anthony Baratta. We each had one of our sons with us. When we eventually made it to Newfoundland, we dropped in on Alice and were treated like visiting nobility. One thing that definitely was not impaired was the cooking center in Alice's brain, wherever that is. Unassisted, she prepared and served dinner for ten. Friends of Alice took good care of us in our 24-hour stay in Newfoundland. Her personal physician, Dr. Pandhi, took us on a tour of the local hospital. While we were there, a reporter for the local paper interviewed Alice and myself and wrote a front page article for the Gulf News entitled, "Doctor Makes 900 Mile House Call To Visit Oldest Surviving Brain Tumor Patient." In the interview, I stated that, "I think we're blessed here with good luck. I would like to think that it was my skill but that would not be proper. It was simply good luck plus, as we say in medicine, "good protoplasm." I attributed her success as part of a certain characteristic found only in Newfoundlanders.

The Canadian Broadcasting Company, hearing about our upcoming visit, had interviewed me by telephone the week before. When asked if this was not indeed a miracle, I told them that we doctors refrain from using that term, but certainly it was unusual. The longest glioma patient reported from a Montreal series of twenty-five patients survived eighteen years. In my own personal experience, twelve years was my second longest survival.

I hoped to visit Alice again in Newfoundland, and I anticipated she would be coming to Long Island, not only for a check-up, but to visit her old friends that she made here during her years on Long Island. Coincidentally, one of her closest friends was diagnosed with multiple sclerosis within the same month that we diagnosed Alice with that brain tumor. I would have thought the chances of both of them being alive thirty years later were one in a million, but here they were, both doing quite well, thank you very much!

As Joe Ransohoff would often say, "It's nice to be good, but better to be lucky."

Chapter 24

Sorry, Doctor, You Made A Needless Trip
(Story of Dawn Skinner)

Late in the afternoon of June 12, 1973, I received a call from the Brookhaven Hospital Emergency Room. I heard the ER nurse say, "We have a nine-year-old girl here, Dr. Bloom, struck by a truck. She's in really bad shape with a terrible skull fracture. Come as quickly as you can."

I drove the seventeen miles to Patchogue in less than seventeen minutes, including red lights. I probably could have talked my way out of a speeding ticket in case a cop caught me traveling at 85 m.p.h.

As I came into the emergency room, the nurse said apologetically, "I tried to call you to stop you, but you had already left your house. It's too late, nothing can be done. She's being pronounced right now." She was told by the emergency room doctor to catch me before I started out since the child had deteriorated so hopelessly.

"You don't mind if I take a peek, do you?" I asked.

"Of course not, if you wish," she answered as I passed her desk.

The emergency room doctor looked puzzled as I removed the crudely-applied gauze dressing. The little girl was without a pulse and had stopped breathing. Some brain tissue oozed from a horrible wound. The x-rays showed extensive skull fractures, with considerable depression of bone fragments. Since the undertaker would have to clean up her head anyway, I figured there was nothing to lose by teasing some of the visible fragments away with a clamp. I released some blood clots, and suddenly, she took a breath! We rushed her to the operating room, and I began removing additional bone fragments, blood clots and dead brain tissue, effectively reducing pressure inside the skull. Gradually, the little girl's breathing improved and her dilated pupil became more nearly normal. She remained in a deep coma for a few days but then gradually regained consciousness over the next several days. By that time, she began to walk.

The grandmother of Dawn Skinner, the little girl, happened to be the chief nurse of the hospital's operating room. She was known affectionately by one and all as "Granny" and was tuned into what was happening to Dawn throughout her entire hospitalization, even though she had not been there during the surgery. Dawn made steady progress day by day, and walked out of the hospital in three weeks. Both her mother and grandmother were ecstatic. So was I.

I followed her recovery and progress out of my office for the next eighteen years. Her main problem was seizures. She was prone to convulsions from the brain scar. Despite prescribing various medications, we could never completely control the unpredictable seizures. We performed several additional operations on Dawn to attempt to provide her with a solid skull using a metal plate. Later, Dr. Milton Tuerk, a senior plastic surgeon, helped me out by swinging a flap of normal scalp over the injured area.

By the time she was seventeen, Dawn was taller than me (and much prettier). She was a striking figure of a young woman who would grab me and hold me tightly as she kissed me every time we met. I was never embarrassed by this when she was ten or twelve years old, but now that she was an attractive young woman, I wondered what the other patients in the waiting room would think, and I suggested that she restrain her enthusiasm.

When she was in her early twenties, Dawn came to see me

again. Normally, her mother escorted her everywhere, but not this time. She told me she was pregnant and intended to raise the child herself. Shades of Linda Drake, I thought.

Somehow Dawn's pregnancy had a protective effect on her epilepsy. I did not try to talk her out of having her baby. She seemed as though she knew what she was doing. Maybe God would protect her, and I was not about to interfere. Her mother expended enormous parental energies bringing her up.

Besides convulsions, poor Dawn also suffered severe asthmatic attacks. By the age of twenty-six, she had been admitted to the hospital a total of thirty times. Often, the asthmatic attacks would bring on convulsions.

I had to ask myself the question, "Would Dawn mature sufficiently to be a good parent in five, ten, or twenty years?" I couldn't answer the question at the time. One thing I always admired about Dawn was the way she never let her epilepsy interfere with her social life. She told all her friends, male and female, what a seizure was all about and how to protect her for the few minutes that she would be unconscious.

One day, I wrote Dawn a personal letter expressing my curiosity about her since years had passed since her pregnancy. In her return letter she sent a beautiful picture of her five-year-old daughter with the appended notation: "The little girl in this photo would never have been born if you had given up." That stirred my curiosity even more. Eventually, I met with her and her child, Alexis Joan.

In August of 1999, I received an invitation for a barbecue in Dawn's back yard with a note to bring my grandchildren to raft on her pond.

"Do I still get a kiss?" I asked when I arrived.

"Yes, from my daughter," she responded coyly. "From me you get only a quick bear hug. After all, I wouldn't want to embarrass you!"

Alexis Joan is now nine years old, the exact age Dawn was when I met her in the emergency room of Brookhaven Memorial

Hospital. They live with Dawn's parents, and "Granny" is now ninety-one yeats old and is still going strong.

I've seen many epileptics in my day, but none so determined to make the most of her life as Dawn Skinner.

Visiting her home constructed four generations ago by her great grand-father, I felt a special feeling urging me to commune with God. I like to feel it was His will that I did what I did on June 12, 1973.

On June 30, 2000, I paid my most recent "house call" and Dawn put me on the phone with Granny, who I hadn't talked to in many years. She reminded me that, in her opinion, I was the calmest surgeon on the hospital staff. She made me feel great since I always thought of myself as a bundle of nerves and a frenetic worry wart. Obviously, I had come a long way since medical school when I was thought of as a "nervous surgeon."

Of course, that's what I would want in a surgeon who operated on me. I would want them to be like a duck gliding on water, smooth and calm on the surface but underneath, out of sight, paddling furiously.

Chapter 25

Ah, Medical Politics—Is It Worth It?

Las Vegas, Nevada 1974

How nice to be here for free, including room and board, airfare, and a hundred and fifty dollars as "honorarium." I even set aside twenty dollars for the one-arm bandits. It was hard to avoid them.

I found myself here for a symposium on malpractice, a formerly obscure legal term rapidly becoming a household word! Two doctors were listed as honored guests, Malcolm Todd, president of the American Medical Association, and Otis Bowen, governor of the State of Indiana. The remainder of the speakers, including myself, had expressed public opinions on the issue.

Bowen had the appearance and demeanor of a small town businessman or administrator, not exactly a flashy guy. I began listening with moderate interest. His homespun manner was unlike that of any politician I've ever heard. Within two minutes I was sitting on the edge of my seat straining to hear every word, every phrase.

This man, I told myself, is endowed with a combination of extraordinary common sense and sheer intellectual brilliance, both concealed until he speaks. He is made of the stuff that made America a great nation—a throwback to our spiritual forbears. He grows on you as you follow his reasoning, and then you follow him wherever he wants to take you. How lucky is the Hoosier State, I thought to myself.

As governor, he dealt with the malpractice issue in a way that brought results. Surgeons in Indiana paid only one sixth the premium that New York surgeons paid.

Wow, New York could learn from Indiana! In fact the whole nation could learn as malpractice insurance premiums skyrocketed nationwide. Now, how could I get this man to New York to teach us how it's done?

At a cocktail reception I chatted with Governor Bowen, praised his statesman-like manner of doing things, and invited him to New York State.

"I'd be glad to come—under the proper auspices of course," he replied.

There is a natural tendency of residents of the Empire State to assume it is provincial America that needs to be taught. *The New York Times* editors tell Washington what government should do, and this extends now to the entire world. The medical profession in New York State differs little in this respect.

When I suggested to our state medical society officials that much can be learned from Indiana the answer was "Indiana is lucky—they have a doctor as governor."

History was to record, in my mind, at least, that our state medical society did not really want to learn from the Indiana experience.

Doctors, brilliant individually, engage in a form of collective stupidity when it comes to influencing government. They lose most of their "battles."

As president of my county medical society, I invited Otis Bowen to visit and tell us "how he did it." Our state society officials all attended, pleased to help host a visiting dignitary.

But learning from him, uh oh, that was something else! The Empire State Complex would not allow MSSNY, an organization that looks for all the world like U.S. Congress in session when its delegates hold their annual convention, to learn.

Although we pushed through a resolution for supporting doctors for public office, this was totally ignored. A family practitioner from Schenectady and a retired neurosurgeon from the central part of the state would have been perfect for running for governor. They were flattered by my suggestion that they run, but there was not a chance of a snowball in hell that any serious effort would be made by the state society, an organization seemingly run by doctors but actually run by several lawyers, just as the state legislature is run by lawyers.

The journalist Jimmy Breslin observed that corruption in government favoring the legal profession is built in, as though notarized. Breslin, in his own way, was merely recapitulating what one of New York's best governors, Herbert Lehman, said a half-century earlier about lawyer-legislators. They "perpetuate for their profession the obstructions to justice by which they prosper."

In retrospect, New York State did not benefit by Governor Bowen's visit. New York's screening committees for malpractice were set up by the trial lawyers lobby, containing no court reporter, the only thing that keeps everyone honest. Nothing is admissible in court that was said by the members of the screening committee. New York screening committees were "just for show" and lasted only a few years; obviously, they were worthless.

We had our friends, Lester and B.J. Van Ess, put up the Bowens during their two day visit. We took them fishing for flounder and on a helicopter ride over The Great South Bay, courtesy of the Suffolk County Police Department. Our county executive declared May 19, 1977 Governor Bowen Day in a welcoming ceremony. My wife, a former professional singer, sang at the reception. and it was, all in all, a grand celebration.

The four of us—the Van Esses and the Blooms—were guests of the Bowens in 1980 at the Governor's mansion during the Indy 500 weekend. On the way home my wife turned to me and said, "I never want to come back to Indiana!"

I was totally shocked by her statement. "Didn't you enjoy

the weekend?" I asked. "It was one of the best in living memory!"

"That's exactly the reason! We've never had it so good. I don't want my memory of Indiana to get diluted. This has been as good as it's ever going to get!"

Dr. Bowen/ Coroner Bowen/ Assemblyman Bowen/ Speaker Bowen/ Governor Bowen turned into Secretary of HHS Bowen in President Reagan's cabinet where his budget of $340,000,000,000, larger than the military, was exceeded only by the Government of the United States and the Government of the Soviet Union. He was America's best physician statesman of the twentieth century with the possible exception of doctor/ general/chief of staff of the army/Governor General Leonard Wood, who ran for president in 1920 in the Republican primaries.

Shortly before his death, Nelson Rockefeller was asked by Lester Van Ess why Otis R. Bowen was never put up as a presidential candidate by the Republican party.

Rockefeller, who himself aspired to our highest office, responded instantly: "The Republican party is simply not that smart!"

The medical profession, who provided this budding nation four signers of the Declaration of Independence, has steadily reduced its civic activities presumably to allow for increased medical responsibilities. How ironic that medical doctors delude themselves into thinking they can buy and lobby their way through the minefield of politics! How tragic they fail to learn from the Indiana example and Dr. Bowen himself. Sometimes I feel the myth of the "powerful doctors' lobby," a public delusion, is shared by the physicians themselves.

Chapter 26

Bullets in the Brain

I had studied neuropathology (pathologic conditions of the nervous system), at Mt. Sinai, New York University, and Yale but never encountered a lecturer of the calibre of Kenneth Earle of Bethesda at the Walter Reed Army Hospital. He knew how to take a dull subject and make it exciting. He had also had been officially involved in the investigation of the death of President Kennedy.

As Dr. Earle explained it, a rifle bullet at 1900 feet per second traveling through the brain causes total destruction of all brain tissue about fifteen times the diameter of the bullet, whereas a twenty-two caliber bullet at three hundred feet per second has a shock wave of little consequence. This was studied by the US Army at San Antonio by setting up gelatin encased in plastic and firing bullets through it at various speeds. The gelatin was roughly the consistency of brain tissue.

The same rifle bullet passing through a person's thigh could fracture the solid femur bone, even from a full inch away. The "shock wave," a factor often unconsidered, is about as important as the missile causing it. That's why a neurosurgeon should know, whenever possible, the nature of the ballistics involved, Kennedy's brain tissue was all over the back seat of the car and the first Lady's dress. This was, quite mercifully, kept from the public by the media.

There was not the slightest chance that President Kennedy could have survived. All of the world's physicians and scientists could not have reversed the situation. Theoretically his heartbeat and blood pressure might have been maintained a little longer, if you call that being alive. It is helpful in the case of a presidential assassination to have some extra time to transfer power to the vice president, and prepare the public for the bad news.

Okay, how about Robert Kennedy, who had a twenty-two caliber bullet enter the brain in the his cerebellar region? Up to five twenty-two caliber bullets have lodged in a patient's brain with both survival and function. Normally they travel at about three hundred feet per second, one sixth of the velocity of a rifle bullet but only one thirty-sixth of the destructive power, which is a function of the square of the velocity. Why, then, did Robert Kennedy die? During his operation, I underwent a live interview by WBAB, a local radio station. I was told Robert Kennedy had been shot in the head with a pistol, had been able to say a word or two and was undergoing surgery that was supposed to last 45 minutes, but had gone on for an hour and a half.

After his death, I learned that the superior cerebellar artery had been injured. Robert, stunned by the impact of the bullet, was concussed but able to react. It was the bleeding artery that did him in. He would have survived nicely if the bullet passed two or three millimeters away, possibly with some loss of coordination, but with no mental or intellectual consequences whatsoever. He could have continued campaigning and might very well have been elected president. He would have spent a few days or so in the hospital for observation with antibiotics to prevent infection.

The same week that Robert Kennedy was hit I had a patient shot in the same location, with the same kind of weapon, the bullet traveling in roughly the same direction toward the cerebellum. The lucky patient had an entry wound of the back of his right ear, about an inch below Kennedy's entry wound. This is where the bone gets hard as a rock, and for that reason is called the petrous ("stone") bone. My patient, a homeless individual, had virtually no brain injury, only minor scalp and bone damage. In his case the bullet was just hanging off the bone and I removed it. It was badly dented out of shape, but in one piece. Lucky Joe walked out of the hospital within days.

Another shooting comes to mind that took place in the sixties. It concerns a fourteen-year-old schoolgirl named Sumi. She attended a Saturday night party where the fifteen-year-old host, demonstrating his father's gun, accidentally set off the loaded weapon. The bullet passed through an open door into the next room and struck Sumi in the back of the skull, entering her right cerebellar hemisphere and lodging at the "tentorium" the infolded dura separating the cerebellum from the cerebrum. The bone fragments and bullet fragments left a clear path on x-rays (this was before scans).

The surgery was easy because there was no possibility of mental deficit, and the most critical area of the right side of the cerebellum was missed by an inch or so. Sumi's coordination was already impaired on the right side and would be alleviated by relieving pressure there. I simply cleaned out the lead fragments and bone chips, removed the dead brain tissue, and closed.

Sure enough, within two weeks Sumi was back in high school, walking, talking, with no mental or intellectual loss and was able to run two or three months later with a barely noticeable loss of coordination. Like RFK she was stunned somewhat by the bullet impact, but never had an amnesia, memory loss or intellectual impairment. The cerebellum is one fifth the size of the cerebrum, but has nothing whatsoever to do with thinking, remembering, cogitating or anything else intellectual.

I have removed the outside half of a cerebellar hemisphere many times. It was hard for me to catch on to this surgical trick. I had always said to myself, "Don't remove normal brain. It has to be there for a reason, even if we don't know the reason." Eventually I learned that the outer half of the cerebellum was actually dispensable. You just don't miss it! Unwise as it is to remove normal cerebral tissue, it is perfectly OK to remove cerebellar tissue.

Robert Kennedy would have done as well if the bullet had lodged a mere quarter of an inch behind. How do I explain about bullets in the brain? It is a complex subject, even in teaching young neurosurgeons. One thing that must be stressed is that there is no burning need to get the bullet, as though, somehow, the bullet is the evil spirit that must, at all costs, be exorcised. Of course the bullet <u>did</u> the damage getting to the final resting place. The damage that has been done may or may not be reversible. If something can be done to improve the patient, surgery is worthwhile. This, of course, is not always the case.

In the late 1960s I was called to the Southside Hospital emergency room to see a man who, according to his wife, "just don't act right, he's not himself." The man seemed alert but curiously disinterested in his surroundings or what was happening to him. The tip-off was a small wound on the left side of his forehead about an eighth of an inch long. We ordered an x-ray and, lo and behold, he had bone fragments extending into the left frontal lobe of his brain associated with bullet fragments. The main part of the bullet went one and one half inches into the brain, a low-caliber bullet obviously.

The wife had observed this curious behavior, but had no knowledge that there was a shooting. The tiny wound in his scalp could have been from a fall with a bump on the head, let us say against a sharp corner.

I explored the man's head and curiously it was the easiest bullet wound operation I ever performed. The twenty-two caliber bullet caused bleeding in the left frontal lobe, the blood clot enlarging to the size of a plum and burrowing right up to the lining of the of the brain. As I enlarged the bullet-hole opening in the dura, the operation finished itself. Like a baby being delivered, the pressure build-up within the brain expelled the entire clot and with it the bullet, pieces of bone that had been embedded and a few lead fragments. I caught the entire mess in a medicine glass and realized after irrigating with saline that the operation was really over! All I had to do was close the scalp.

The man improved and became more alert within the next three days. He could now remember what had happened. Apparently he was caught in flagrante with a married woman and shot by her jealous husband. Consciously, or otherwise, he did not tell his wife about it or did not remember it. I was never quite sure which explanation applied.

There is a very good reason why self-inflicted gunshot wounds must be treated as though they were accidental. A severe brain injury causes memory loss. Two of my self-inflicted gunshot wound patients had their suicidal memories erased entirely in the same way the old lady of "Happy Mistake" had her suicidal memory erased by her concussion when her husband cut her down. One of them was an "aging" bachelor who, on his fortieth birthday, shot himself with a twenty-two caliber rifle. I first operated to clean up the injured brain and later for a subdural hematoma caused by the exit wound of the bullet striking a vein on the surface of the brain, causing slow bleeding. I sent him off to rehabilitation and a year later learned he had made a complete recovery. This was similar to the Robert Adler case, except this was a forty-year-old man rather than a seventeen-year-old. I had a similar reaction, I was surprised by the news that he had made such a complete recovery, but not at all surprised that he had no memory of his suicide attempt.

The other case was a thirty-year-old man whose father was a personal friend of mine. Having heard a parental argument, he placed a handgun to his mouth and fired. His mouth had to have been very wide open. The bullet went up through the hard palate, through the nose and the base of the skull close to the brain stem and through the entire left hemisphere from floor to roof, the bullet lodging against the inner table of bone. One reason I remember this case well is that, although I was in charge, one of my colleagues stuck his nose in and told the father of the young man that his life was not worth saving since he would be simply too impaired. The father, not easily intimidated, replied, "if you don't mind, my wife and I would prefer that everything be done that can be done."

One of the problems here was a spinal fluid leak coming from the base of the brain into the patient's mouth. Fortunately, it sealed itself off without surgery. I made the decision not go for the bullet since I believed that there was nothing to be gained by subjecting the patient to such surgery even though it had gone entirely through the brain and would be easily reached from the top of the head. After two weeks the young man was out of ICU, the spinal fluid leak having subsided with no infection. He had a mild right sided paralysis, a speech defect, and problems with the eye muscles, most of which cleared with time. He went on to become self sufficient as a carpenter and I followed him for many years even after the death of his parents.

There is a bit of humor attached to this grisly story, I'm happy to report. My all-male social club on Monday nights heard me say, "I saved a life today."

"What happened?" they asked.

"I didn't operate," was my response. Everyone broke into uproarious laughter. Later I regretted saying it, since they would constantly allude to my innocent statement, always reminding me of the life I saved by not operating!

It is wrong to predict what is going to happen unless one has considerable experience with bullet wounds of the brain. I remember taking care of a fourteen-year-old boy shot through the brain similar to the case of James Brady. It entered the left side of the forehead and came out on the right side of the brain toward the back of the head.

The boy allegedly stole a car, and he was running down a detective in a parking lot. The detective shot through the windshield and the bullet went entirely through the brain, and lodged just under the scalp, having penetrated the back of the skull as well. The boy was in coma, and I didn't think too much of his chances, but went ahead in routine fashion, irrigating out dead brain, blood clots and bone fragments, both from the back of the head and in the front. Later, I had to take him back to the Operating Room for abscess formation.

Six months later, I was surprised when I saw how well he was doing. He had regained speech and the use of his limbs much faster than Mr. Brady, undoubtedly because of his youth. The weapon, I believe, was at least a .38 caliber bullet and, in this case, the main body of the bullet was easily reached under the skin when I operated on the back of the head.

I cannot stress the great advantage of youth, not only in dealing with bullet wounds, but in virtually all pathology of the brain. On one occasion some twenty years ago, a freak accident occurred when a policeman's revolver went off as he was placing it in his holster. The bullet went through the floor and struck his two-year-old child on the floor below. I operated and removed dead brain, blood, etc., without going after the bullet. *Newsday* thought it was interesting that I performed surgery, but without any intention of removing the bullet, and headlined the story "MD: Bullet to Stay!" Going after the bullet is, of course, utter nonsense. If the main fragment of the bullet is removed, it is only because it is simply available and accessible, but it is not the primary reason we operate on bullet wounds of the brain. In this case, the bullet penetrated through both frontal lobes of the two-year-old, and I predicted that there would probably be no intellectual impairment, since at this age losing 1 to 1½ oz. of brain tissue can be well-tolerated.

This brings me to the final story about bullets in the brain, and it involves another tragic accident involving a policeman's gun. The fifteen-year-old son, left in charge of his father's revolver and presumably intelligent enough to take care of the gun properly, somehow didn't carry out his responsibility. There were two other sons, much younger. The five-year-old son found the gun, pointed it at the two-year-old boy (his younger brother) and said, "Bang, bang, you're dead." He pulled the trigger of gun. Unfortunately, the gun was loaded.

What a horrible tragedy this turned out to be. I saw the two-year-old boy in the Emergency Room at Southside Hospital, where plain x-rays of the skull showed an intact bullet lodged in the brainstem. That alone seemed incompatible with sustained life. There were three holes in the boy's head for some reason. Perhaps, the bullet went in, came out and ricocheted back into the boy's head, lodging in the brainstem. It is highly unlikely that the five-year-old fired three times or even twice, but this is all speculative and incidental to what happened next. I was quite sure that the child would die, and I merely wrapped bandage material loosely around the head, awaiting his death.

As it turned out, I had misjudged. The boy did not die, and after two days, we realized he was decompressing dead brain from the three openings in his skull, and was not about to die unless we deliberately neglected him. It was necessary at this point to take him to the operating room and clean up the various wounds and treat him as though he was going to live.

What kind of child would he be? How badly retarded would he turn out? How much cerebral palsy could we expect?

Surprisingly enough, the child did very much better than we expected. He really is a miracle case, and I followed him for fourteen years. At age ten, he sent me a picture of himself and on the back signed "I love you, Dr. Bloom". That touched me deeply.

I found it necessary to place metal in one of the three openings in his skull to protect his brain. The other two openings healed by themselves He was slowed down in terms of intellectual growth by this horrible accident no doubt, and yet he managed to walk, talk, write and get involved in sports. At age fourteen, a baseball struck him right in the part of the skull that I had put the metal in, and I had to repair the dent. That was the last I saw of this boy, truly a miracle child.

This young boy is alive for two reasons- (1) because I hadn't wrapped his head tightly, and by decompressing himself, he managed not to die of increased pressure; and 2) I didn't operate and close the three holes in his head. He literally expelled most of his damaged brain tissue through the openings in his skull. He was a healthy normal appearing boy at age fourteen. Time erased virtually all of his deficits. Did I ever do anything to save this boy's life? Absolutely not. Perhaps God saved him. I merely bumbled through it all. It was, quite literally, a case of saving a life accidentally by not operating. Had I operated on the first day to close the three skull openings, the pressure build-up would surely have killed him.

Do neurosurgeons agonize about whether death is inevitable, or preventable? Of course they do. With experience, we learn better what to expect. Life is full of surprises. It is our duty, however, to minimize them, and to properly advise patients and their families to the best of our ability and within the limits of our knowledge and experience.

Chapter 27

Where Can a Guy Get Pronounced Dead Around Here?

When does death actually occur? In New York State, the most backward of the fifty states on this issue, you are legally dead when the body is cold and decaying, without heartbeat, without brain waves, without movement, and without someone looking to indict you for murdering the corpse by pulling the plug.

When a 21-year-old weight lifter burst a blood vessel in his brain and deteriorated steadily, I did my best to reverse the tragedy, joined by a very capable colleague, Alan Rosenthal. Our surgical efforts at Brunswick Hospital failed, and I pronounced the young man, Doug Firestone, brain dead. Within a day or two, the parents, justifiably anxious for a funeral, were told by a hospital administrator they needed a court order to have the life support systems discontinued.

The judge, Theodore Velsor, did not grant the petition of the parents but instead scheduled a hearing several days later. I was asked to be there and noticed that the court room teemed with journalists.

Called to the witness stand, I gave testimony. The district attorney asked me why I didn't just pronounce my patient "dead" instead of simply "brain dead," and get it over with.

"Because of people like you," I responded, "who might enjoy

indicting me for murder."

This had happened in California a year earlier, I reminded the now-hushed courtroom. The New York State Legislature had consistently refused to pass a brain death law and remains one of the last states in the Union to cling to outmoded beliefs on death pronouncements.

Incredibly, the Firestone family had worked out a plan for an ambulance to carry their son's corpse with the attached breathing equipment to the enlightened State of Vermont.

There the doctors weren't any smarter, just less fearful of district attorneys. After the plug was pulled, Doug's heart would stop minutes later. A Vermont doctor could then pronounce Doug dead and sign the death certificate. Then they would travel another 200 miles back to Long Island with their son, now an official corpse, and proceed with burial.

This was the only legal way for the family to proceed. There was another way, practical if not legal. Mr. Firestone would hold his left hand in Mrs. Firestone's right hand and Mrs. Firestone's left hand would hold the next person's and so forth, and there would be this daisy chain of fifteen or twenty people, all crammed into Doug's tiny hospital room, ready to share the legal responsibility for pulling the life-support plug. A mass-murder would be about to take place, meaning a mass of twenty people were about to murder a person, who, in another state, would be legally dead.

Mr. Firestone would reach under the bed and with his right hand pull the plug. This would be the time to get the posse out and round up those twenty vicious murderers before they escaped. Shouldn't the distinct attorney nail these cowardly criminals and put them behind bars for life, the penalty for pre-meditated murder?

Just as the family and close friends were getting serious about committing this "dastardly" act, Doug's heart stopped by itself!

The way I look at it, even from the Great Beyond, Doug couldn't bear to see his parents and their friends enduring life sentences and mercifully willed his pesky, mischievous heart to stop beating.

All this happened in Amityville, New York a few years ago, and I applaud the parents of Doug Firestone for their courage and advanced thinking processes. Most families are sheep-like regarding the "Law" when a loved one is dying.

As it turned out, the law was never passed, but the legislators are off the hook. State judges came down hard on murderers who said that no, they didn't kill their victims, they only caused them to be in a brain-dead coma. The doctors, nurses, porters, or whoever pulled the plug on the machines, they were the real murderers.

The judges were forced to finally clarify the law by their own actions. Now we no longer fear being charged with murdering the already-dead corpses with the beating hearts.

My fellow neurologists, neurosurgeons, and others have committed hundreds, perhaps thousands, of murders if one interprets the law as Dennis Dillon did. This long-serving Nassau County District Attorney considered a beating heart a sign of life and anyone who promoted stoppage of this organ was a murderer.

Somehow, I've never felt the least bit guilty about pulling the plug when the Harvard criteria are satisfied and all the family are in accord. It is technology that has created corpses with beating hearts. Human hearts continue to beat as long as two months after the brain has died taking with it the personality, the character, the persona, and yes—the soul.

On the material side, consider that two months of unnecessary intensive care could add an additional half million dollars to the hospital bill!

The Empire State, a leader in technological innovation, a repository of the best of American civilization, center of the universe to many, is curiously backward the handling the issue of determining when death occurs.

Chapter 28

As Good As The Old Egyptians

It was in little old Seaford General Hospital, where I had done so much spine surgery over the years. Like all other Long Island Hospitals it constantly tried to become better, offer more, do the right thing. One of the members of the medical board decided to pass a rule that no brain surgery could be conducted at Seaford General Hospital. The motion was carried. The reason: "We are a small hospital and do not wish to do anything for which we might be sued."

That sounded good, and not only to the medical board. I myself normally transferred patients out to one of the hospitals better equipped for brain surgery.

One day I received a call from Howard Sacher, a colleague on staff. Would I see a lady who was getting drowsy and take care of the problem if it were neurosurgical? Her CT scan showed a large collection of blood between the brain and the skull bone.

As soon as I got to the lady, it became obvious that she was deteriorating rapidly. It would be too risky to get on the phone and start looking for a better equipped hospital.

I put her on a gurney and personally wheeled her to the operating room where I flashed the CT scan before Elsie, the old time nurse who was in charge at the time.

It was late afternoon, the day's surgical schedule having been completed. Fortunately for the patient, an operating room was instantly available. Elsie, always doing the right thing, made me write on the chart that it was a life and death emergency. I started shaving the patient with the electric razor, removing her hair and putting it in a plastic bag. In case the patient dies, the person's hair is presented to the undertaker.

Elsie asked, as I was quickly scrubbing my hands, "How do you propose to get through the skull? As you know, we don't have any skull instruments."

"Just run out to the driveway and find a sharp stone and boil it up. That's the way the ancient Egyptians did it three or four thousand years ago. A sharp stone will scrape bone away. We're just as good as those old Egyptians, aren't we Elsie?"

Though I was joking, our minds were busy trying to figure out how I would get through one third of an inch of bone. "How about a hammer and chisel, say a small chisel?" I said, thinking out loud.

"How about a curette?" Elsie said. She referred to an instrument used for abortions and for scraping bone.

I followed Elsie's advice. In the meantime, I injected some local anesthetic and cut down to the bone inserting an instrument to hold the skin apart. The curette simply wouldn't get through the outer layer. After trying a few other instruments, I went back to a curette, this time a much smaller one and slightly sharper. I just scraped and scraped away until, finally, I got through the hard outer layer of bone. Now we could proceed with a bigger curette. Sure enough within another couple of minutes we were through the bone and there was the dura, colored blue from the mass of blood behind it. A little nick with a sharp instrument and three or four ounces of blood evacuated itself.

The lady made a remarkable turn around. Maybe it wasn't so remarkable for those of us who have done this many times, but it was dramatic for all concerned who hadn't seen this sort of thing carried out. The lady was speaking sensibly by the following day, and walking within two or three days. By the ninth or tenth day she walked out of the hospital in quite decent shape. Dr. Sacher, the family, the patient, and myself were all quite pleased.

About a week after the patient left, I encountered Elsie, my scrub nurse, in the hospital cafeteria. There was a huge smile on her face.

"Oh, Dr. Bloom, By the way, I found two or three stones in my garden that would be just right for your next cranial case."

I picked up on Elsie's jest. "That's great," I replied. "Hide it somewhere where no one will see it. After all," I said, rolling my eyes a bit, "we mustn't carry out brain surgery in the Seaford General Hospital!"

Chapter 29

The Mendizabel Story

One of my early tragedies bothered me for many years. It was a six year old girl being taken to her dancing class by an elderly neighbor. With girlish enthusiasm she leaped out of the car and dashed into a small space between the front of the car and a metal fence. The driver accidentally stopped the car in gear and the car lurched forward crushing the little girl's skull. She was whisked into the Smithtown General Hospital and I was called to see her.

The x-rays showed her skull had been badly crushed. I took her to the operating room as quickly as I could and began removing the massively depressed fragments.

Whether I could have saved her life had I been quicker, already on the spot or whatever it would have taken, I do not know and shall never know. The girl died on the table, and both the mother and the driver of the car had some sort of transient nervous breakdowns. I won't forget Fred Fischler, the family doctor, entering the operating room and asking about "the accident." I did not take the time to notify the family or anyone else since I thought that every second counted.

After the death of the girl, I was a little nauseated and could not eat my lunch when I returned to my home, something that never happened again. Perhaps I became tougher as I faced each consecutive tragedy.

Now it was twenty years later. I was about to conduct my

office hours when Ravi Shetty, a personal friend and neurologist, called me early one afternoon and described a bashed-in-skull in a thirty-five year old man. I remembered the dead little girl that I wondered about so long ago.

"Ravi, get him in the operating room as fast as you can and tell everybody I'm on my way!"

I almost literally ran through my waiting room where five or six people were waiting to see me, shouting, "Life or death emergency—sorry." I sped to the hospital in Amityville, New York, in about ten minutes at eighty miles an hour, scrubbed my hands for ten seconds instead of the usual ten minutes and began removing bone as fast as I could. The x-rays had shown massive and extensive depression of bone severely compressing the brain. This time the patient survived. He came out of coma and improved steadily. Within two to three weeks he was transferred to the Brunswick Hospital Rehabilitation Unit where he spent a couple of months more. He made a complete recovery, apparently. What happened was revealed by the man's employer:

On his first day on the job, working in a garage, the machinery collapsed and an automobile, with its platform, fell on Mr. Mendizabel's head. For a brief period, his fellow employees were paralyzed with fear assuming Mendizabel had to be dead. When the boss arrived on the scene, he had everyone to do their part in lifting the car and the platform off of the crushed skull. The man had recently arrived from Guatemala, and had a wife and children. He was alive, but barely so when the car and platform were lifted off of his head.

I quite sincerely believe that we saved him due to the speed with which we moved. Dr. Shetty quickly got the patient to the operating room, explained the situation to all concerned and he was ready for me to operate as soon as I arrived, a time interval of about fifteen to eighteen minutes from the time I first got the information.

Of course, all this may not by itself prove anything scientifically. In my career there was a third opportunity to prove my point, namely that speedily-performed surgery can save a life in the case of massive depressed fracture of the skull. This took place at Southside Hospital a few years afterwards. That patient also survived and I believe would have died if we had not treated it as a first class, top priority emergency, even more emergent than many of our bleeding cases. Although these three cases in my total experience cannot be considered scientific, but it does, of course, make sense. We know the brain swells rapidly when there is sufficient mechanical pressure as was the case in these three patients. In the case of the little girl that died, I wonder if it were a hopeless situation in any case or whether, let us say if I had gotten there ten or fifteen minutes sooner, could she had been saved? We know that young patients, young children and babies, particularly, can withstand the most brain damage and get away with it.

Chapter 30

Sandy's Close Call

November 18, 1977 was a terrible day for Sandy Ventrice. This young divorcee, and mother of a three-year-old boy, was visiting from New Jersey. She had dinner at her sister's house in Bay Shore and, after the family dinner she decided to take a walk. That is the last thing that Sandy remembers, until she recalls vomiting in a toilet in a strange home.

She eventually would learn that a tall man dragged her into a wooded area after striking her repeatedly with a metal object. The blow to her right temple fractured her skull and left her unconscious. As he attempted to rape her, a rifle shot rang out. At that point, he pulled up his pants and ran.

The assailant did not realize that a young man and his father who were packing their car for a hunting trip were observing him. They heard the tire iron strike the pavement, and saw Sandy being dragged among the trees. The civic-minded family called the police who then picked up the would-be rapist. The perpetrator had blood all over his shirt, and told the police it was from a chicken he had just killed when they picked him up.

The police took Sandy to Southside Hospital a few minutes away. She was conscious and had a deep gash in front of her left ear. A general surgeon stitched it up. An hour later Sandy was in a coma. Her pulse had become slow and the pupil of her right eye had become two to three times as big as that of her left.

I realized what the possibilities were when the emergency room doctor called.

"Send her to the operating room at once!" I told him.

I realized Sandy was bleeding from a little artery on the right side of her skull, that it was enlarging rapidly and compressing her brain, and that she would be dead if we delayed. There was no time to bother with tracking down the family and getting consents. Even getting a scan on her would be valuable time lost.

Lois, the O.R. nurse, made me write a note on the chart that this was a life-or-death emergency.

I normally scrub my hands for eight to ten minutes but shortened this one to a few seconds and let Lois glove me. I had shaved enough hair in front and above Sandy's right ear to make my incision. By this time she was decerebrate, her arms and legs stiff, in a really deep coma.

Drilling my burr hole I was greeted by current jelly clot that I suctioned away. Now it was time to remove more bone from Sandy's skull. I suctioned away four to five ounces of fresh and clotted blood, and found the bleeding artery. I cauterized it, and did the same for some veins in the area. Dr. Arikian, my assistant, pointed out that her limbs were looser and that her pupils were nearly normal.

It was time to talk to the family, I never got to speak to them earlier, and I am happy I didn't bother to try, since every minute counted. The initial blow to Sandy's head caused a minimal brain injury from which she was recovering. In the meantime, the cracked bone, with its sharp edge, nicked the little artery, creating a clot growing in size and rapidly compressing her brain.

When the collection was grape-sized it wasn't big enough to cause symptoms. A half-an-hour later it was probably the size of a plum and in another twenty minutes or so it was the size of a slightly flattened lemon. This is what I encountered as I suctioned away the blood clot. Had it reached the size of a medium orange to a large orange Sandy would have likely died. How the patient does depends on how fast this condition, known as epidural hematoma, is diagnosed and properly treated. Obviously timing is all-important.

Sure, Sandy made it, she left the hospital within two weeks. She was still weak in the left arm but able to walk. Mentally, she was not quite okay. Within the next six months to a year Sandy regained all her faculties. Her hair also grew back. She was constantly involved with the police and the district attorney's office. Since no penetration could be proven it was not classified as a rape, merely as an assault.

The newspapers kept Sandy's name from the public. Her family took care of her son. About six months after her assault I attempted to restore the contour of the skull using wire mesh made of stainless steel.

Some time later, Sandy became one of the file clerks at the x-ray department in Southside Hospital and remained on the job for fourteen years. This helped me to see her often and to keep up with her progress. This also reminded me of my good judgement. Had I wasted time trying to notify her family, it would have taken much longer for her to recover, assuming that she lived.

Eventually, Sandy married an engineer. Her sister, Yvonne Perez, still works in Medical Records at Southside Hospital. Another sister, Arlene Perez, is in the business office, and her son, more recently, became an employee of Southside Hospital.

Her assailant, a man on parole, had been convicted many times for assaults and robberies. His original explanation about the source of the blood on his shirt originating from cleaning a chicken turned into a claim that he struck her because of a racial slur she used after he innocently asked her for a cigarette.

Never did a word take place between them. Sandy never even saw him when the steel weapon wielded by her attacker struck her twice on the head with the metal object. The parolee was sent to jail for five years. It would have been 20 years to life if Sandy had died from her epidural hematoma.

Chapter 31

Don't Give In To The System

Mr. Schulz, my attorney, pronounced his evaluation of the situation in a professional, but very matter of fact tone of voice. "I suggest, Dr. Bloom, that you allow us to settle this case for you for the full amount of your policy, that is to say, $100,000. Excuse me for asking, but how could you have been so careless as to have only $100,000 worth of insurance? You're fortunate that Rosensweig, the orthopedic surgeon, had a million, and he's willing to part with $500,000. That, with your $100,000, will keep the plaintiff happy."

"Why should I let my insurance company give anything at all? I've done nothing wrong," I insisted.

"Well, you never know how juries are going to react," Mr. Schulz replied. "My advice is to settle."

I said nothing further but mailed Mr. Schulz a certified letter, return receipt requested, insisting that we go to trial so that my innocence could be proven. Not long afterward, Mr. Schulz, myself, the judge, and a court reporter gathered in the judge's chambers.

"Mr. Schulz," asked the judge, "Exactly what is your complaint here?"

"Your honor, Dr. Bloom is setting me up for a legal malpractice. He failed to follow my advice and sent me a certified letter."

"Dr. Bloom, what have you to say about this?"

"I say that I will not allow my insurance company to pay out any money, inasmuch as no malpractice exists."

"All right," said the judge, "you have one month to get another attorney, Dr. Bloom. You, Mr. Schulz, are no longer a part of this lawsuit."

One month later, I had a new attorney, one whom I respected highly and who was in full agreement with me that there was no good claim for malpractice. Another month and we were in the court room for the start of the trial. The plaintiff was a law student on whom I had operated several years previously for a disc herniation in the cervical spine. This was done from the back leaving a scar on the back of his neck. Within a couple of years, he, for some unexplained reason, developed an abscess in the lower spine. The gist of his lawsuit was that the abscess came from a spinal tap that I had performed earlier, and the abscess left him paraplegic, and he would never be the same.

The insurance company had hired a surveillance company to observe this person, and they found he could walk fairly long distances, going to and from his classrooms. His attorney was happy to suggest that the man had been paraplegic when in actuality he had probably been a little weak from his abscess. The fact that he made a recovery was not emphasized.

The most interesting part of the trial was when we, the defense, put on a handwriting expert who proved to the jury that the plaintiff had perjured himself. The plaintiff, in "sworn testimony," described a man with the same initials who he said lived with him. Apparently, he needed to get credit rating and invented a man, giving a complete description of him, before the jurors. The handwriting expert, one of the best in the country, pointed out how the loops were the same for the plaintiff and his "tenant," the imaginary young man.

These two days of testimony knocked the stuffing out of the plaintiff's case and his own attorney, in a moment of general despair, shocked the rest of us when he said, "I feel like I've been sleeping with a diseased woman!"

Naturally, I felt a little saintly, having saved the insurance company over half a million dollars. You would think that they would have the courtesy to send me a letter of gratitude, but of course, insurance companies just don't work that way.

Chapter 32

The Loaded Question

We neurosurgeons no longer have to be good doctors, although most of us are. The neurosurgical community regards itself as secondary (or even tertiary) care providers, superspecialists of course. We invent new operations and are ready to perform them, as long as somebody pays the bill. Usually it's an insurance company.

For about a decade or more, insurance companies paid— rather heavily at that—bills for surgery done to prevent or alleviate strokes. The surgeon would hitch up an artery in the scalp to an artery in the brain called the middle cerebral artery. This artery would get plugged up for one reason or other, and the idea was to get blood beyond the point of obstruction to "irrigate" the part of the brain that needed the blood.

But doesn't the brain die from lack of blood in a matter of minutes? Yes, but it didn't seem to make a difference. Once insurance began to "cover" this questionable surgery, most major neurosurgical centers got on the bandwagon, and it seemed perfectly kosher. No one saw fit to "prove" that the operation worked for many years.

Then, suddenly, the world was awakened by a scientific report that proved the operation was of no value. At a meeting in Toronto, we were presented with careful, meticulously prepared material by Dr. H. Barnett, a Canadian neurologist, who proved, with little question, that the operation did not benefit the patients. Many neurosurgeons in the audience grumbled and regarded the paper with stunned disbelief.

I personally was thrilled inasmuch as I didn't buy the reasoning behind the surgery, known as a superficial temporal artery-middle cerebral artery anastomosis, and I had met Dr. Barnett a few years earlier in Vail, Colorado. He had conferred distinction on the hitherto little known center in London, Ontario, along with Charles Drake, the father of basilar artery aneurysm surgery.

Within a year, the insurance companies realized that the operation, now discredited, did not have to be paid for. Sure enough, this form of sophisticated vascular surgery was dropped like a hot potato.

Should neurosurgeons look for ways to get out of doing surgery?

Not if they wish to be rich and famous—only if they feel a close link to the human race as a learned member thereof, genuinely concerned for its welfare.

I recall a meeting of one of our national societies where I attended a luncheon seminar about broken necks with injured spinal cords. Five or six of the well-known professors of neurosurgery participated and in the question-and-answer part, I got in the act, as a member of the audience.

"What would you do personally," I asked the panel, "if you were present when someone near to you and dear to you dove into shallow water and became instantly quadriplegic?"

The professors were stunned by the question. They didn't answer. Obviously, the situation had never come up, but even more obviously, they hadn't even thought about it. Finally, one muttered to another, half under his breath, "That sounds like a loaded question." Quietly, they decided the conference was at an end, and slowly filed out. Although they had two aisles to choose from, they all moved toward the one furthest from me.

There wasn't anything at all "loaded" about the question.

The reason I said "someone near to you and dear to you" was to eliminate the fear of malpractice, such as might occur if the victim was a stranger. Unlike the professors, I had thought of what I would do. The same as I would want done to me if I were the victim—the instant application of manual traction to my head.

A ten-year-old boy can accomplish more at the scene of this type of catastrophe than the entire neurosurgical community an hour later in a trauma center, if ideal first aid were properly carried out for traumatic neck dislocation with cord compression.

Ideal first aid is never recommended in the emergency manuals, and the neurosurgical community has made no sustained effort to change things. "Why get the public involved?" is their attitude, and besides there are too many legal implications.

Well, okay, I speak—or rather, write—as an individual. If a member of my family dislocated his or her neck, I would move at once to grab the head cupping my hands, one under the chin and the other under the back of the head. Then, I would gradually start pulling the head away from the body with about 10 or 15 pounds of force. I would make no sudden change in either the amount of the pull or the direction. The direction should never change along the long axis of the spine.

When Dr. Heimlich described his now famous maneuver, he realized that thousands of people were dying for lack of knowledge of proper first aid, and proper aid has to be done instantly, not by professionals in a hospital setting. There simply isn't the luxury of time when someone is choking and turning blue! Anyone interested in saving a life could learn the maneuver, physician, nurse, bricklayer, concerned parents, people with compassion, total strangers, it makes no difference!

And anyone who would like to attempt to prevent permanent paralysis in someone with a dislocated neck can do so by applying slow, steady traction on the neck. The partially paralyzed are more likely to respond than the totally paralyzed, but you must not use excessive force.

The spinal cord is just as soft as the brain and, like the brain, dies with prolonged pinching in a short time. The delicate neck vertebrae are easily dislocated when the body moves through space and the head strikes an immovable object. The momentum of the body causes the neck bones to dislocate, pinching the spinal cord, and causes paralysis of the legs and weakness or paralysis of the arms. And when should the unpinching take place? Of course, the sooner the better. I believe this should be a public and public health issue.

Christopher Reeve lives on while General Patton, with a similar injury, died, and there is good reason for this. Reeve was younger, but mainly his accident occurred five decades later. When Patton, a quadriplegic after a jeep accident may have lacked the will to survive as a totally dependent cripple, he also lived in a different era. Rehabilitation of spine injuries had not yet become well-developed.

Kenneth Turk, a Denver neurosurgeon, told me that his neurosurgical nurse, bringing in a trauma victim on a plane/ ambulance, radioed that her patient was losing the use of his limbs. Dr. Turk ordered early traction and the nurse complied. The limb weakness cleared by the time the plane landed in Denver. That is but one example of what early traction can do!

I don't expect a high percentage of the American public would want to learn how to reduce neck dislocations on the spot, knowing that only a fraction of the cases would be successful.

But think of it this way: your son, your granddaughter, your niece, your best friend just dove into shallow water and became suddenly without the capacity to move the limbs.

Sure, you can call the ambulance and let the learned people take over, according to standard and accepted practice. No one will accuse of you of stepping in where angels fear to tread.

But with 15 minutes of formal training, you can accomplish at the scene of an accident more than all the world's scientists put together a half hour later, if you "unpinch" the injured cord and, by realigning the dislocation, restore the vascular supply and prevent infarction, tissue death.

Once an Amityville physician witnessed his neighbor become quadriplegic when he failed to "duck" adequately driving his tractor into his garage. His head was caught and his neck dislocated. The physician, the late Dr. Joseph Gestal, bravely rushed to the scene and pulled on his friend's neck until the ambulance arrived. Then, he carefully switched to halter (cloth) traction using weights. I also rushed to the emergency room a half hour later and went into my act, instant tong application, more traction, later fusing his spine. Did I help him? Yes, but not nearly as much as his family doctor. We pulled the man through and he eventually walked, but 80% of the improvement that did occur took place while Dr. Gestal was pulling on his neck. All my sophisticated maneuvers, as I reflect on this case, while standard or proper, were far less important than Joseph Gestal's brave actions undertaken early. Dr. Gestal, with his early manual traction, did far more than I did by unpinching his pinched spinal cord. Both the patient and Dr. Gestal described total quadriplegia at the beginning of this tragic accident. Their descriptions match.

These and other anecdotal situations suggest what ought to be plain common sense. I hope at least some of the readers are sufficiently intelligent and modern to want to learn how to do what, in my opinion, really ought to be done. Even if only a dozen people a year are spared a lifetime of paralysis by early and courageous action, this anticipated "discussion" will be worthwhile.

Chapter 33

Deborah Ribbe—Wonder Woman

Author's Note: This piece presents the surgeon's version of a story about Deborah, which originally appeared in the *St. Petersburg Times*, written by Richard Verrier, a much better writer than myself.

It was August 9, 1987, when Deborah Ribbe had her brush with her maker. It was a clear Sunday night on Long Island. She and her best friend had just returned from a wedding shower and were driving to her boyfriend's house after having some drinks at the Oak Beach Inn. Debbie had a good job as a hairdresser and had recently became engaged. Being a bride-to-be made her excited, but that night, however, destiny had other plans for her.

Debbie lost control of her car, knocked over a telephone pole and crashed into the side of a house. Debbie's friend was removed from the car by the emergency medical technicians, but Debbie could only be extracted by cutting a hole in the roof of the car with a chain saw. When the technicians got to her, one reached for her pulse and could not get one. She wasn't moving or breathing. A sheet was placed over her entire body.

Several minutes later, somebody noticed Debbie twitching. Almost instantly, they were en route to Good Samaritan Hospital, and a number of doctors were called, including myself. Her jaw was broken in at least two places. The right eye socket was crushed. Jagged glass had slashed various parts of her body.

When I arrived at Debbie's side, I noted there was pressure on her brain from a depressed skull fracture and took her to the operating room at once. I quickly shaved her head, after she had been intubated. The doubly-fractured jaw bone hung down to her lower neck. I removed various bone fragments and also a blood clot that had been forming inside her head.

Deborah's family soon arrived, and we discussed her condition. We could not, of course, predict the outcome, but we did know that Deborah would need her family more than ever.

We had to tracheotomize Deborah because of her horrendous jaw fracture and her long-term comatose state. It would be unwise to leave the endotracheal tube in place for more than a few days or so.

Over the next month, Deborah gradually emerged from her comatose state. She could not talk, of course, because of the metal tube in her windpipe, but even if she had a clear breathing passage, she probably still would not have made sense. Sadly, Debbie's communication skills had been damaged in the accident as well. This condition was demonstrated when a piece of paper that contained the words "We love you" written by her parents was passed to Deborah. Deborah took a pen and scribbled gibberish, something that had no letters but indicated that she was trying to write something. As the weeks went by, she improved slowly but steadily.

Eventually, the tube was removed, and she began to walk with assistance, particularly from the physical therapists.

From the standpoint of Debbie's parents, it was a nightmare. Her father, a former New York City fireman, and also a school bus driver for a time, thought she looked like a Martian. Her mother agreed that it was one big nightmare and in her first entry into her diary wrote, "God, please help our Deb and our family through this."

During her hospitalization, when Debbie's coma seemed to be impossibly long, they placed a small piece of cloth, symbolizing the shroud that Jesus Christ was buried in, over Debbie's arm and began to pray. Debbie squeezed her parents' hands. To them it represented a miracle indeed. That was the first in a series of signs that she could communicate with them. The lower jaw was wired shut and when consciousness improved, they used a chalk board to communicate, as well as squeezing the hands.

Debbie's brain injury was such that she was confused and disoriented and would throw a tantrum every now and then. She had to be tied down by the nurses so that the tubes that kept her alive wouldn't be pulled out. At times, she would even try to strike her parents. Her father started taking tranquilizers.

After a month, she was transferred to a rehabilitation center. Like a child relearning to write, walk, read, speak, and play with blocks and coloring books, it was a gradual emergence and replay of life itself. Her parents now realized that they would have to raise their daughter all over again, something that many parents have been obliged to do when their child has had a horrific brain injury.

Debbie had total amnesia when it came to remembering the accident. She had to be told of it repeatedly. She remembers being shocked by the mirror appearance of herself. In fact, her parents covered the mirror in her room with tape so that she could not see herself, but Debbie pulled her wheelchair up to the mirror and actually pulled the tape off! During the course of her recovery, her parents played music from her favorite band to help her emerge from her comatose state. Music therapy has been very popular since it was discovered in Great Britain that music aids in the recollection of memories, particularly in people who are music-oriented. Debbie's therapy continued for months, and the day that we told her she could stop taking dilantin for seizures, she celebrated, but by getting drunk. She then had an argument with her fiancee and the two split up.

Debbie moved back to Florida to live with her parents and start a new life. She joined an alcoholic support group and learned how alcohol had cost her her job, her fiancee, and almost her life. She was able to shake the drinking habit and gained new found friends. As she put it, "I found a God of my understanding."

When she began to get her physical coordination back, she set up her own program of exercises, dancing, more dance lessons, and just plain walking. She found that without alcohol, she could even dance better than before. In Port Richie, Florida, she even won a free-style dance competition. Later on, she decided she would go to college. This was her own idea since her parents were not so sure that she could handle life on her own just yet, but she was extremely serious about attending school and put all of her energies into it.

In May 1995, at the age of 31, Debbie graduated from Pasco-Hernando Community College with a degree in Human Services. She was one of the top members of her class.

Her remarkable recovery and her iron will to make a new life for herself has given Debbie a heroic aspect with her family and friends. They are now proud of all she has accomplished.

And I am proud to have participated in Debbie's rebirth. I truly admire the grit shown by her parents and congratulate them for their steadfast devotion. Although we doctors and nurses have contributed to her rebirth, Debbie's parents deserve by far the most credit for having brought Debbie up all over again.

Chapter 34

Coleen Colligan

As her name suggests, Coleen Colligan was as Irish as one can get. She possessed a broad and ready smile, a love of people, and an appreciation of wine and song. Though her parents were staid, Coleen was prone to carrying her extroverted nature to extremes. At least she did this with some of her male friends. They were wild, tough, and often rowdy. Coleen was to learn the hard way the price sometimes exacted for belonging to such a group.

When Coleen was twenty years old, she was involved in an accident that nearly cost her her life. Her date was driving while inebriated, and they sailed through the main street of Amityville, Long Island, going south at 60 miles per hour, double the speed limit. Where Main Street forks there was a clock tower statue, set in nine tons of rock, a fairly immovable object. The impact of less than two tons of automobile that ploughed into the tower utterly destroyed it and deprived Amityville of one of its time-honored landmarks.

Considering the physical factors involved, it is most remarkable that either Coleen or her companion remained alive. They were removed to the emergency room of Brunswick General Hospital, a few blocks north. The worst injuries were sustained by Coleen herself. Her skull and facial injuries and her two fractured ankles, all taken together were not nearly as serious as the compression fractures of her lower spine, squeezing the lower tip of her spinal cord.

At first, it was difficult to tell whether Coleen had trouble moving her legs because of the ankle fractures or because of the spinal cord injury. I had been called in as part of a team of trauma surgeons. The orthopedist, Dr. Chewaprong, was concerned and rightly so. Within a day or two, it was obvious that two thirds of the spinal canal had been obliterated in cross section at the mid to lower spine. This showed clearly on the scans. Her spinal cord had to be compressed. Coleen required a catheter to drain her bladder. Her rectal sphincter (the circular muscle of the anus) tone seemed impaired, looser than normal. I told Coleen and her mother that I thought it would be wise to decompress the spinal cord surgically. They consented, and we proceeded. It was the third day of her hospitalization, and she had stabilized in every way. The time was right.

Dr. Chewapraug assisted me at the surgery. It went smoothly. As soon as we opened the bony structures covering the spinal canal, the coverings of the spinal cord moved up toward us. We knew we had created more space and felt optimistic about the outlook. There were no small fragments of bone penetrating the cord. We proceeded to close the muscles over the space we had created. Up and down, we had removed the bony covering of three adjacent vertebrae.

Coleen had nowhere to go for some time. She had extensive casting for the ankle fractures and could not, in any case, be expected to walk for six to eight weeks even without a spinal cord injury. During this time, she steadily regained the use of her lower extremities. At four or five weeks after the surgery, we removed the catheter from her bladder. The urologist attending her, Dr. Yu, followed her for at least the next ten years.

Although, Coleen never regained full control of her bladder, she did improve steadily then leveled off with a mild but permanent problem. Most importantly, she could walk, get about, and look after herself.

I have followed Coleen's recovery these many years, often telling her how proud I am of her because of how remarkably well she has done. Five years ago, she called to inform me that her mother had died of a ruptured aneurysm and that she was now free to take me to lunch. I didn't understand and asked her to elaborate. Coleen then told me that after she was able to walk, she asked her mother if she could invite me to lunch to show appreciation for helping her regain the use of her legs.

"Oh no," her mother replied. "You don't take your surgeon to lunch." Coleen respected her mother's wishes on this matter up until the time her mother died.

She invited me to a delightful restaurant in Huntington Village where we came closer to knowing each other as people, and not merely doctor and patient. Coleen was attractive, well-spoken, and I asked her if she would join me on a television program with the talk show host, Joel Martin. With Joel, I had discussed public education regarding both drunk driving and spinal cord injuries, and he agreed that Coleen would be perfect for demonstrating what can happen to careless teenagers.

The day was arranged, approximately three weeks after our luncheon. The show was taped in a Viacom studio in Hauppauge, Long Island.

Coleen was calm and poised. She had the aplomb of an actress and spoke with absolute authority. She described her temporary paraplegia and her various other injuries. She was effective in cautioning viewers about the dangers of drunk driving. All agreed she gave a sterling performance, and I told her so as we dined immediately after the taping. Coleen pledged herself to be available for any event involving public education that Joel or I could come up with in the future. I was grateful to her for helping me with what I thought was the duty of every doctor—to contribute to the education of the community-at-large on important health matters.

Observing Coleen Colligan socially, I found she has learned from her own misfortunes. She undoubtedly can fend for herself quite nicely but, like the rest of us, she also needs a certain element of good luck.

In 1998, she was down on her luck with boyfriend trouble and an urgent need to move. Short on cash for a down-payment for a new apartment, we made a deal. I loaned her money, and she became my part-time receptionist. She worked off every last penny and currently works in a similar capacity for a medical group. Put her in a crowd and she makes the crowd come to life.

Long after we became friends, we discovered that I had treated Coleen for a brain injury at Central Suffolk Hospital when she was only five years old. I told Coleen, "That's it! One brain injury and one spinal cord injury! That's all the neurological care you're getting out of me," I joked.

Chapter 35

Dead People Don't Breathe

It was 8:30 in the morning at the Sheraton Hotel in Hauppague, Long Island.

"I'm looking for Mr. Shamoun," I said to the desk clerk.

"How would you describe him," he asked.

"I would assume he is in his fifties. I have never actually met him," I answered. Just at that moment I heard my name called.

"Doctah Blo-oom?"

I was taken aback by a young man in his early thirties who, obviously, was the local Melvin Belli of the southern city he came from, having won more than one hundred million dollars in verdicts for his clients. We sat down to discuss the events that would take place over the next seven hours. As a neurosurgical consultant no longer in active practice, I am available to lawyers, insurance companies and government agencies, or anyone else who can benefit from my expertise.

A group of attorneys from the southern city would be arriving soon for a deposition. Shamoun advised, "Don't be floored by them. They act like members of a country club. So don't let yourself be in any way denigrated or bamboozled by these fellows."

I must confess that, at the beginning I wasn't terribly excited about Shamoun's client, the family of a young man who was shot through the brain and sent off from a hospital to the morgue, still breathing. The morgue people decided after two hours that a dead person should not be breathing like that and sent him back to the hospital he came from.

The second admission of the patient was weird for many reasons. How often does a patient arrive at the emergency room of a hospital from a morgue? The chart was full of strange notations and did not make a lot of sense. There had been an obvious attempt to cover-up and virtually everyone involved disagreed with one another. I had been studying the depositions of the defendants and was preparing as an expert witness for the plaintiffs.

One of the cover-up details was that the patient was sent out breathing but "in a terminal fashion", such as an occasional gasp. Further review of the records, however, indicated that the breathing was regular both before he was sent to the morgue and after he arrived there. Five defendant attorneys represented various doctors, the hospital, and some of the nurses. After a couple of hours of intensive drilling I was asked to describe my understanding of the patient's breathing.

"In and out, in and out, in and out," I replied. I was then interrupted and there was further discussion about breathing and at a certain point I simply said, "A five-year-old child knows that a dead person is not supposed to be breathing!"

"Well I've had enough," said one of the lawyers as he stood up and began to stride out of the room. "I have been wasting my time here and I don't know why I came in the first place." Off he went without looking back.

Shamoun leaned over and whispered to me, "He has to catch a plane at about this time and would have left in any case. He just wanted to hit you with a parting shot."

I was all set to go south for the trial to give testimony in the courtroom, but an out-of-court settlement was reached between the plaintiff and the insurance companies of the defendants in the amount of five hundred thousand dollars.

Am I pleased with the outcome? Does it make me happy?

I am pleased with how I handled myself, but not with our legal/judicial system, where money and winning the case is of greater importance than true justice. We are less a nation of laws than a nation of lawyers.

Chapter 36

We Stand On Their Shoulders

All my professional career, I have, along with my colleagues, stood figuratively on the shoulders of our distinguished predecessors. Great pioneers in medicine and in surgery have paved the way for those of us who did our thing in the latter half of the twentieth century. Foremost in the ranks of great neurosurgeons is Harvey Cushing, born April 8, 1869 in Cleveland, Ohio. Cushing's father and grandfather before him were physicians.

In studying his early life, I found that this multi-talented individual could express himself very well in the detailed letters written to family or friends. In addition to his literary skills, he provided ink sketches of sailing ships, camels, donkeys, and whatever he saw on his excursions to various parts of the world. Later, he would continue his artistic skills in recording what he saw at surgery. His hospital charts were filled with drawings of his operative findings, and of course, so were his books and numerous scientific articles.

He was captain of his baseball team at Yale, and the nimble young man could do a back flip off an elevated ledge and land on his feet. Of course, these were not the talents that made him famous, but he was naturally proud of all he could do and was not bashful about flaunting it.

In his histology notebook that he kept in his first year at

Harvard Medical School, there were drawings so professional that one would assume these were the works of a trained medical artist.

While still a medical student, he introduced Roentgenograms, later known as x-rays, to Boston. He also introduced the so-called "ether chart" to increase safety during surgical operations. No physician I am aware of can match these great contributions made as a medical student.

Cushing felt an inexorable urge to travel everywhere. He visited Victor Horsley in London and decided he could do better than his famous British predecessor, the first surgeon to perform only neurosurgery. I have often used Horsley's bone wax, a substance made of bees wax, to stop the skull from bleeding during surgery. Absolutely safe stuff, used for over a century.

Cushing was originally quite close to his resident, Walter Dandy, at Johns Hopkins. Dandy, a brilliant and talented young doctor working for Cushing in the Hunterian Laboratory, did basic research on the brain cavity and hydrocephalus. Cushing, after sixteen years at Hopkins, had been recruited by Harvard and the new Peter Bent Brigham Hospital and planned on taking Dandy along as his assistant. When he started to pick up some papers that Dandy had written, Dandy simply took the papers out of his hand, stating that he, not Cushing, was the owner of the papers. Affronted by the impudence of his young junior, Cushing had a change of heart. Dandy would not accompany him to Boston. Dandy was suddenly left stranded without a job.

As both men went on to become great pioneers and innovators, this "controversy" continued over the next thirty years or more as long as both great men lived. I have to sympathize personally with Dandy. I respect Cushing immensely, but I believe he was afflicted with a tendency to be unreasonable. It went along with his colossal egotism, well deserved perhaps, and his yearning to be number one at all times, traits not unique among great men. Cushing set out to become a great star in the history of medicine and surgery, and succeeded. He became famous internationally as the father of modern neurosurgery.

Of course, there is also room for Dandy's star. I have no doubts that Walter Dandy was even a superior technician in the operating room than his former boss. It does not matter to me who did what to whom, or why. There is plenty of room in the night sky for both their stars to shine.

Dandy explained hydrocephalus and the ventricles. Cushing explained acromegaly and the pituitary gland. Dandy discovered that tumors of the eighth nerve could be totally removed, shaming Cushing, who didn't believe it. Dandy, the only neurosurgeon ever to be nominated for a Nobel Prize, introduced the injection of air to outline the brain cavity in 1917 and 1918, a test that Cushing was loathe to use simply because it was Dandy who invented it.

Cushing refined the electrocautery for neurosurgery. Cushing showed that a mortality of under 10% for brain tumor surgery could be achieved by a careful neurosurgeon, a stunning historic first that gave great impetus for the emerging specialty. Both Cushing and Dandy wrote endless papers and books. Cushing definitely was the leading man in terms of reputation and influence.

We live in a different era now, where so much is taken for granted and yesterday's miracles are now regarded as mundane episodes. It is all too easy to overlook the genius of our professional forebears and their huge contributions to medical advancement.

Cushing died in 1939, about seven years after he moved from Boston back to New Haven, where he served as Sterling Professor of Neurology. Harvard and Yale both had fought to harness his glory ever since he finished medical school. Johns Hopkins had him for about fourteen years. The whole world has his legacy.

Thomas I. Hoen, my own mentor, trained with Cushing. This allows me to think of myself as Harvey Cushing's professional grandson!

Cushing's only son was killed in a motor vehicle accident a short time after Cushing had bought him a car, the single great tragedy of his personal life.

Cushing's scientific honors are numerous. Incidentally, he also won a Pulitzer Prize for the two-volume biography he wrote about his good friend, Sir William Osler. Osler and Cushing were immediate neighbors in Baltimore. Each had a key to the other's house indicating how close the friendship had to have been. One or the other would always have visitors from various parts of the world, and it was always easy to have the next door neighbor join in the celebration. Osler, the older of the two, is regarded as the father of modern medicine world-wide. It is reasonable to assume he "rubbed off" on his junior comrade and helped mold him into the father of modern neurological surgery.

It is Walter Dandy, who had a bigger heart than Cushing. Cushing went out of his way to make life tough for Dandy. He must have been jealous of his onetime trainee. Twentieth-century neurosurgeons were a bit slow to honor Dandy fully. Not until the 1980s, about 40 years after his death, did he receive the full recognition he deserved.

In 1954, I met William Sharpe, a neurosurgeon who trained with Cushing even before Dandy. Sharpe owned a country estate in the Adirondacks where I worked as a general practitioner. I loaned him my secretary, Roseann Welch, to type the last chapter or two of his book, *Brain Surgeon*, published by Viking Press in 1955.

This colorful character not only invited me to his Adirondack home but had me to tea in his Chinese gazebo on a small island on a pond behind his house in St. Petersburg, Florida. It was connected by an ornate oriental bridge to the "mainland," an appropriate setting to allude to his 1910 sojourn as a Professor of Surgery at Peking (now Beijing) Medical College, and his operation on the emperor's son, the same one portrayed in the movie *The Last Emperor.* He told me how the boy's mother plotted Sharpe's death by poisoning if her son, prime heir to the throne, was to suffer in any way from his surgery, removal of a small clot under the skull where the boy had been injured.

The grateful emperor held a great feast to celebrate the surgical triumph, had Sharpe sit next to him, slipped him an envelope during the festivities, and all concerned proceeded to become howlingly tipsy. On the following morning, Sharpe was showering, recalled the envelope, dashed from the shower, opened it and counted Chinese currency that amounted to $54,000 in American money, over a million dollars in today's equivalent currency. Quite a tidy sum of money for little more than a burr hole!

Sharpe said he may not have operated if he knew the patient's mother's penalty for failure. I agreed with him, and laughingly told him I didn't anticipate any problems with palace intrigue when I became a full-fledged neurosurgeon!

Sharpe recalled a number of stories about Cushing. On one occasion Cushing had two or three assistants to his home for dinner. Apparently frustrated by his inability to achieve a measure of cooperation on the part of one of his daughters, Cushing got up from the dinner table and took his plate with him out into the living room, alone, pouting and visibly disturbed.

"Now you get back here, Harvey," ordered Mrs. Cushing, and Cushing meekly obeyed. According to Sharpe, this thrilled the dinner guests, all trainees who knew Cushing, typically, as the one to shout the orders and who expected them to be followed instantly. In his own home, things were obviously very different.

That Cushing was a taskmaster is not a subject of debate, but sometimes the martinet would carry things a bit far. On one occasion, he accused Sharpe of lying to him.

According to Sharpe, who was six feet four inches tall and built like a bull, he became totally enraged by the accusation, grabbed his boss by the collar with his left hand until he saw Cushing turn pale, then wisely released him, realizing he might have overreacted. He was not fired, but on the other hand, he was assiduously ignored by Cushing, who never did anything to promote Sharpe's career after that incident. Not that Sharpe needed help, he could make it on his own.

As an undergraduate at Harvard, Sharpe tutored a wealthy fellow student who was physically agile, socially overactive with a tendency to neglect his studies. He was Franklin Delano Roosevelt. After polio crippled him, Roosevelt was no longer the same person. He took life very seriously. History would have paid little attention to him were it not for this tragedy, it seems.

After becoming the president of the United States, the grateful Roosevelt had Sharpe's *Textbook of Neurosurgery* placed in all federal and military hospitals with medical libraries. For a time, I owned a copy of that textbook and must admit that, for its day, it was not a bad text. In any case, Sharpe was never accepted into the mainstream of neurosurgeons, once the societies began to form. He remained on the outskirts or perhaps a trifle beyond, to the end of his days. He was close to only one other neurosurgeon, his brother Norman, junior co-author of the textbook and sometime partner in surgical practice.

Sharpe suffered a stroke in his late seventies, and his wife, Josephine, brought him to me. I took care of him at University Hospital, NYU. It was 1958. He died of complications of his stroke.

Standing on the shoulders of early pioneers like Cushing, Dandy, and Penfield, and those I learned from directly such as Jefferson, McKissock, Hoen, Malis, and Ransohoff allowed me to see further than I ever might have on my own and helped people like Dawn Skinner, Rosario Ricci, Linda Drake, Robert Adler, Alice McNeil and many others survive circumstances that otherwise might have claimed their lives.